Home Office Research Study 261

Substance use by young offenders: the impact of the normalisation of drug use in the early years of the 21st century

Richard Hammersley, Louise Marsland and Marie Reid
Department of Health and Human Sciences, University of Essex

The views expressed in this report are those of the authors, not necessarily those of the Home Office (nor do they reflect Government policy).

Home Office Research, Development and Statistics Directorate
February 2003

Home Office Research Studies

The Home Office Research Studies are reports on research undertaken by or on behalf of the Home Office. They cover the range of subjects for which the Home Secretary has responsibility. Other publications produced by the Research, Development and Statistics Directorate include Findings, Statistical Bulletins and Statistical Papers.

The Research, Development and Statistics Directorate

RDS is part of the Home Office. The Home Office's purpose is to build a safe, just and tolerant society in which the rights and responsibilities of individuals, families and communities are properly balanced and the protection and security of the public are maintained.

RDS is also part of National Statistics (NS). One of the aims of NS is to inform Parliament and the citizen about the state of the nation and provide a window on the work and performance of government, allowing the impact of government policies and actions to be assessed.

Therefore –

Research Development and Statistics Directorate exists to improve policy making, decision taking and practice in support of the Home Office purpose and aims, to provide the public and Parliament with information necessary for informed debate and to publish information for future use.

First published 2003
Application for reproduction should be made to the Communications and Development Unit, Room 201, Home Office, 50 Queen Anne's Gate, London SW1H 9AT.
© Crown copyright 2003   ISBN   1 84082 958.3
                          ISSN   0072 6435

Foreword

This report is one of five research reports published as part of the Vulnerable Groups Research Programme. The central focus of the programme was to investigate patterns of drug use among groups of vulnerable young people and their access to services. Each project focuses on a different group of vulnerable young people, who tend not to be included in general population surveys. The project reported on here concentrates on young people in contact with youth offending teams. The four other projects examine: young people involved in sex work; homeless young people; young drug users who are in contact with drug services; and young people leaving care. Many of the young people across these projects are likely to have had similar backgrounds and vulnerabilities. A number of the studies explore this area and the degree to which the young people are in fact the same population caught at different points in their lives and via different services.

The main aim of this study is to examine the prevalence of substance use and offending amongst young people who are clients of Youth Offending Teams in England and Wales. It has long been suggested that substance misuse and delinquency develop together and that similar risk factors, such as a disrupted family background, associating with delinquents and having difficulties in school, predict both behaviours. However, drug use has now become more common amongst young people, and is not necessarily coupled with the previously identified risk factors. Therefore, there is a need to examine this 'normalisation' of drug use amongst young people with regard to young offenders and how the relationship between drug use and offending has been affected as a result of this.

Tom Bucke
Programme Director, Drugs and Alcohol Research
Research, Development and Statistics Directorate

Acknowledgments

We would like to thank all the young people who were interviewed at length for this research, as well as our team of field researchers: Gail Castle, Paul Dellimore, Sonia Desborough, Michelle Ellis, Tony Goodman, Gareth Hewitt, Ronno Griffiths, Peter Kenninson, Steve Kenny, Mags Lyons, Martin Moran, Brian Pearson, Pete Smith and Elaine Wilkinson. Also the Youth Offending Teams in Bolton, Cardiff, Cheshire, Colchester, Hounslow, Oldham, Merthyr Tydfil, Richmond, Sheffield, Stoke-on-Trent and the Vale of Glamorgan, as well as the New Martin Consortium Youth Trust. Thanks also to Andrew Oliver for help with the data. Acknowledgement is also due to the Economic and Social Research Council, which has funded a second wave of interviews as part of the Network on *Pathways into and out of Crime: Risk, Resilience and Diversity* (Grant L330 25 3001), directed by Derrick Armstrong, School of Education, University of Sheffield. We would also like to thank Gary Mundy and Tom Bucke of the Drugs Research Unit, Home Office for their thoughtful and sympathetic guidance of this work.

Richard Hammersley
Louise Marsland
Marie Reid

The Drugs and Alcohol Research Unit at the Home Office would like to thank the independent assessors for this report.

Contents

List of tables and figures

Executive summary

Aims and methods

This report describes results of a survey of young offenders' substance use, self-reported offending and related risk and lifestyle factors, using an extensive structured questionnaire. Nearly 300 interviews with Youth Offending Team (YOT) clients across England and Wales were achieved.

Profile of the cohort

The cohort comprised predominantly white males age 15 and 16, although females were represented proportionally to their appearance as YOT clients, and black and Asian ethnicities were deliberately over-represented. Generally speaking, few characteristics of the cohort varied systematically with sex, age or ethnicity.

The final sample over-represents those with longer offending histories and those who had greater involvement with the YOT; young people on final warnings without attached requirements and those whose case and other work occurred entirely away from YOT premises were unlikely to be interviewed. Thus, this cohort is not representative of all young offenders and findings are likely to exaggerate the severity of substance use and offending amongst young offenders.

Two key characteristics of the cohort emerged:

- Many had been excluded or had dropped out from school before age 16, most left school without qualifications; a considerable proportion were in neither education nor employment.
- The most common past and current family circumstance was for young people to live with their mother only; a greater proportion of this cohort lived in lone parent households than in the general population.

Traits and experiences

A range of variables was explored because of their potential to influence substance use and offending: coping mechanisms, self-esteem, school affiliation, sociability, plans and expectations for the future, parenting and life events and problems. Key findings were:

- A large minority, particularly of women, had low self-esteem. Collectively, the cohort did not use many positive coping mechanisms and a large minority used alcohol or drugs as escape coping.
- The majority did not like school or get along well there.
- The cohort had low, but typical, aspirations for adult achievement, but many expected to get into trouble with the law again.
- The young people tended to see friends regularly, mostly close to home, and also dated regularly.
- Multiple life events and problems were common. Over half of the cohort had experienced at least one of the following: school exclusion, parental divorce/separation, a family member with a criminal record, bereavement. Nearly a quarter had been a victim of crime in the previous two years.
- Despite the frequency of life events and problems almost half the cohort would keep their feelings and problems to themselves.

Service use and service involvement

Service use and involvement were investigated as indicators of psychosocial problems and to provide information about unmet service needs for young offenders:

- GPs and Social Work were the most common services used, although more than one-half of respondents had visited an A&E department during the previous two years.
- More than one-tenth of the cohort felt they needed special help with education and/or getting a job and had not received any.
- The quality of help received was generally felt to be low; over 40 per cent said it had been only better than nothing or no use at all – except for help with getting a job. Only half those who had received help for a drug or alcohol problem felt it had been useful.

Offending and substance use

Offending and substance use were investigated and it was found that:

- Most had committed at least six different types of offence during their lifetime, and over 20 per cent reported shoplifting, selling stolen goods and taking a car without consent at least 20 times in the previous 12 months.

- Over 20 per cent also reported committing drug dealing type offences at least 20 times during this period.

The prevalence of drug use in the cohort was extremely high:

- The self-reported prevalence of all drugs exceeded that reported in the Youth Lifestyles Survey and in the British Crime Survey 16 to 30 cohort (even without correcting for the fact that the present cohort are relatively young and would be expected to use drugs less than people in their 20s).
- However, the cohort contained relatively few heroin or crack cocaine users and use of these drugs was not generally that frequent. Instead, the cohort tended to use alcohol, cannabis and tobacco extensively, along with other drugs less often.
- There were signs of the 'normalisation' of drug use in that the cohort used a wider range of drugs, younger, than would have been the case 20 years ago. Moreover, this diverse drug use did not indicate a progression or funnelling towards heroin or cocaine use. Instead, heavier users tended to use alcohol and cannabis frequently and other drugs occasionally.
- Drug use and offending in this cohort may represent a period of intense misbehaviour, which may or may not be temporary.
- There was no evidence in this cohort for two common media fallacies: that the age of first trying drugs has dropped (although progression to more serious substances has speeded up), and that heroin and cocaine dependence have become commonplace among people under 16.
- There were only 13 drug injectors, who were disproportionately women, had experienced more life events and problems, less parental control and had lower self-esteem than the remainder of the cohort.
- Despite high prevalence of use, few of the cohort reported dependence and only 15 per cent were rated (by ASMA[1]) as at high risk of substance abuse problems. However, 15 per cent is about 10 times the prevalence of high risk youth found in a large school survey.
- Users with more problematic use (assessed by ASMA) were more likely to have been referred to a drug service and/or received other help, but only a minority of those who received help felt it had been useful.
- Forty per cent or more of the cohort felt there was some relationship between their substance use and their offending.

---

1   Assessment of Substance Misuse in Adolescence (Willner, 2000).

Predicting substance use and offending

It is important not to take the sheer magnitude of this cohort's substance use as evidence that it causes or explains their offending. Patterns of offending and patterns of substance use were therefore identified, before exploring how these different patterns relate together, and finally considering other factors that may contribute to these relationships:

- Three factors for substance use frequency were identified: stimulant and polydrug, addictive type, and socially acceptable (alcohol, cannabis and tobacco).
- Socially acceptable substances predicted offending more than the use of other drugs (although the latter were less common and hence less able to predict anything).
- Shoplifting was related to addictive type drug use; stealing from cars and beating people up were related to stimulant and polydrug use. It is likely, therefore, that rather than the classic relationship between offending, heroin and crack use having disappeared, it is swamped by much more diverse substance use.
- Low school affiliation, number of life events in last two years, and lack of positive coping mechanisms predicted offending and substance use.
- Those with more severe substance problems tended to have received more help, but were likely to have made more than a single contact with a substance service only if they were heavier users of addictive type drugs such as heroin, other opiates or crack cocaine.

Discussion and implications

There was evidence of normalisation, and alcohol, tobacco and cannabis were more related to offending than were other drugs. The 'funnelling' towards heroin and/or cocaine use and/or drug injection of delinquents observed in the 1980s was not evident. The fact that drug use by young offenders involves extensive cannabis and alcohol use, means that interventions need to address these substances as well as others.

Some key factors were related to both substance use and offending: life difficulties and events, disliking and being excluded from school, lack of positive coping mechanisms and expecting to get into trouble again. These factors suggest that there is a risk of a vicious circle developing where drugs and perhaps offending are used to cope with life's difficulties, which can make those difficulties worse, which can confirm young people's expectations of getting into trouble again. There is a need for young people to be taught positive coping mechanisms, including those for dealing with past events and trauma.

The cohort felt that they had received quite a lot of help, but its quality was generally perceived to be low. Because of the diversity of substance use in this cohort, it is as well to be wary of generic programmes tackling such problems. Individual counselling or small-scale interventions may be more appropriate.

There is a continued need for generic services to deal more effectively with mid-range substance use problems (Tier 2) without either minimising them or referring them on to specialist treatment. For young patients, GP health behaviour screenings need to consider drugs as well as drinking and smoking, and other generalists, such as social workers, need to enquire routinely about substance use when other problems are evident. Engaging young users with services is a key problem.

There is a need to consider the complexities surrounding the relationship between substance use and other problems in young offenders. This cohort could not be neatly divided into normal substance users without problems and 'addicts' with problems. Thus for most young offenders substance abuse is neither the main cause of their other problems, nor a subsidiary symptom that will naturally vanish when the other problems are treated.

Parents need to be engaged concerning their children's substance use. This may be easier when that use is predominantly alcohol, cannabis and tobacco, rather than focussing on drugs perceived to be more serious. Data from this cohort (who are relatively serious drug users) suggest that ages 11 to 14 are important for drug experimentation. Part of engaging parents will be teaching them a sad realism about the contemporary prevalence of drug use in this age group. This includes recognition that broad experimentation is a common part of adolescent drug use and appreciation that immoderate use of any substance should be of concern.

Many schools adopt a low- or zero-tolerance to drug use. This may not be helpful as it encourages children to conceal, rather than deal with, their drug use and can lead to the exclusion of those caught, who are not necessarily those who use drugs most, never mind the only users in school.

This study broadly confirmed that drug use has become normalised amongst young offenders. This is not to suggest, however, that drug use is a problem-free activity that society is merely prejudiced about. As evidenced by this survey, young offenders drink and take drugs not only more than their peers, but far more than society should approve of, or they should want to. The long-term impact of this remains to be ascertained.

It has become accepted that drug use and offending are associated. Indeed, worldwide almost every survey of these behaviours has found some form of association between them. The survey reported here aimed to:

- document the prevalence of substance use and offending amongst young people who have become clients of the Youth Offending Teams (YOTs) in England and Wales
- survey the frequency of use (as well as the prevalence) of illegal drugs plus alcohol, tobacco and other legal substances including solvents, prescription benzodiazepines and amyl and butyl nitrate, which are also often abused
- examine patterns of substance use amongst young offenders and identify relationships between substance misuse, offending and personal and social risk factors, in the context of the normalisation of drug use
- attempt to identify factors placing young offenders at risk for substance dependence;
- document the service use and service needs of young offenders, particularly regarding substance abuse.

The survey constitutes the first wave of a longitudinal study. The second wave is funded by the Economic and Social Research Council and will report in 2004. Piloting for the first wave began summer 2001 and data collection ran until August 2002.

Terminology about drugs

This report uses 'drug use' as a neutral term to describe all use of substances, whether legal or illegal and will also use 'substance use' as a synonym. 'Problem drug use' will be used rather than 'drug abuse' because in younger people problem drug use may or may not fit clinical diagnostic criteria for abuse (American Psychiatric Association, 1994) and, besides, in practice not all young offenders have been assessed and diagnosed in this way. The report will also mention 'drug dependence', according to standard clinical criteria, but for the same reasons as just outlined, this is of less relevance to the cohort studied here. Finally, 'drugs' is used to cover the wide range of substances commonly taken to enjoy their psychoactive effects, but it is important to be specific about individual drugs and to avoid over-generalising findings applicable to only some substances.

Causes of the association between drug use and delinquency

Risk factors

There have been many surveys of substance use amongst youth, including worldwide a number of longitudinal studies of offending and substance use that have followed young people from adolescence into adulthood, or even from childhood to adulthood (see Robins and Rutter (1990) for introductions to many of them). All find that substance use and offending are associated and that the same constellation of risk factors predict both behaviours amongst young people. Substance misuse and delinquency develop together in a 'common causal configuration' (Elliott *et al.*, 1985). Thus young offenders are a group who are likely to use substances more than their peers. Moreover the combination of substance use with offending may increase the risk of developing substance dependence and/or becoming a persistent offender. Longitudinal studies suggest that common risk factors underlie both substance misuse and other offending behaviour. These include:

- a disrupted family background and low parental supervision
- associating with delinquents
- poor social skills
- having low psychological well-being
- having a history of age inappropriate behaviour
- having difficulties with school
- having been in care
- having been abused.

When these risk factors are present, then substance abuse and delinquency tend to develop together, at the same age and within the same peer groups. In the UK there has been a substantial increase in young people's illicit drug use over the past 20 years with almost the same proportion of females as males having tried drugs (Aldridge *et al.*, 1999). This increase in drug prevalence is unlikely to be explicable by underlying increases in the classic risk factors described above. Drug use is so prevalent among young people that in some forms it may now occur without it being explicable by specific 'risk factors'. Moreover, the prevalence of drug use may in turn complicate the classic association between drug use and delinquency.

So far, reference to problem drug use or drug abuse has been avoided. The clinical definition of substance abuse is use that does not meet criteria for dependence but that still leads to clinically significant impairment or distress including failure to fulfil major role obligations (at school, work or home), recurrent use in physically hazardous situations, recurrent substance-related legal problems and persistent or recurrent interpersonal problems related to substance use (American Psychiatric Association, 1994). A difficulty when considering the substance use of young offenders is that this definition of abuse hinges upon the presumption of the substance causing or worsening the problems. This misunderstands the concept of a 'common causal configuration'.

Take three truants who drink heavily, smoke cannabis daily and fight: their fundamental problems may be quite different. One might have a problem with anger as a maladaptive response to anxiety, caused by trauma. He or she may use alcohol and cannabis to reduce anxiety and fight *despite* those substances. The second may have an alcohol problem, worsened by heavy cannabis use. He or she only fights when intoxicated and is not anxious, so the substances *cause* the fighting. In the third person the two behaviours may not be particularly related. Perhaps they fight at football matches, then drink heavily afterwards, but this is due to their social network rather than a cause and effect relationship. In the abstract, it sounds easy to separate these, but it is complex when working with real people, who may not themselves understand their own behaviour. It is tempting instead to make simplified judgements about 'drug problems' based on implicit norms about which drugs are typically 'problems' and what patterns of use are 'problematic.' Also, as drug use becomes more prevalent, different drug using practices may be judged intrinsically problematic or problem free. There is probably intergenerational disagreement about this.

Different types of cause of drug use and delinquency

Before considering potential contemporary complications, it is important to separate out three different sets of processes by which risk factors cause drug use and delinquency, which have entirely different implications for intervention. This section of the report summarises extensive and complex literature on the development of delinquency, substance use and other problems. The three sets of process can be labelled 'Initiation', 'Intensity' and 'Dependence'. The same risk factors make a person more likely to initiate either behaviour, more likely to be more intensely involved in substance use or offending and more likely to become a dependent career criminal, but the processes by which these factors work are different.

Pathways through delinquency and substance use

Moreover, it is necessary to consider that most delinquents moderate or cease offending within two years of starting. It is less clear what happens to their substance use. Two paths are widely recognised: a downwards path to criminal drug dependence that typifies some people still involved with criminal justice, or drug services, as adults; and in the general population, a normalised path of increased substance use into adulthood, but without increased offending. It is likely that in a cohort of young offenders, other pathways will occur. For example, having had more problems, some young offenders might avoid increasing substance use as they mature into adulthood. Another pathway might be that some moderate offending but are left with drug or alcohol abuse as adults, which continues to cause them problems.

Initiation

People who do not use, or admit to using, drugs are less likely to offend, or admit to offending, than people who have at least tried drugs. This applies even to cannabis or use of tobacco or alcohol by those under 14. Initiation into deviance is a function of:

- A consistent reporting bias, with some people tending to deny, or re-attribute deviant behaviours (see Hammersley, 1994; Davies, 1997; Patton, 2002)[2]. This bias is not simply a form of research error, because how people identify, label and monitor their own behaviours can also impact how they behave. For example, people who label themselves as a criminal, even prematurely, may conform to type. This causes some people to identify themselves as drug users or offenders and others to avoid this.

- Individual differences, so that some people are more attracted to deviance than others, and many people with serious psychological problems also tend to use drugs above base rates. There are a range of relevant individual differences, from personality traits that can steer people towards drugs and delinquency – including sensation-seeking and difficulties handling anger – to severe problems including problems of co-morbidity where the person has a number of different things wrong with them.

- Social grouping, so that people tend to learn both forms of deviance in the same social groups. The four most important social groups for young people in this regard are children who truant, children who are in care, children who are imprisoned and children who hang about together with little parental supervision.

- Reduced affiliation with conventional social activities such as education, activities with parents and religion. Users being both pushed out of conventional activities – for example by school exclusion – and being pulled into deviant ones – for example by being encouraged to offend by other drug users. This results in drug users/offenders having less to lose by continuing these behaviours.

---

2   Processes involved include lying to preserve confidentiality or for other socially functional reasons, forgetting occasional events and re-explaining one's offending or drug use as 'not really' being those activities. For example, some people 'don't really' buy stolen goods, because they don't think about their source. Occasionally drawing on someone else's 'spliff' at a party might similarly 'not really' be cannabis use. The potential magnitude of these effects is worrying for survey research. For example, compared with Customs and Excise figures about 30 per cent of the alcohol taxed in the UK is unaccounted for in surveys of alcohol intake.

- A low self-esteem effect, where people who have been seriously damaged or depressed by life may feel that they have little to lose by taking drugs or offending and may care little about the consequences of those behaviours. A variety of psychological and sociological theories attempt to explain the mechanisms by which this occurs. Low self-esteem causes people to feel less able to change their behaviour because they tend to feel that they are not capable of change, that change is not something they deserve and that the future is bleak anyway.
- Simple opportunity to take drugs or offend. Opportunity arises from the availability of drugs or offending opportunities and the young person having unsupervised free time, for example by being excluded from school while parents are at work.

All the classic risk factors (listed on page 2) potentially influence these processes, either directly or indirectly. The six processes explain why young people initiate drug use and why they begin to offend. Indeed, they over-explain both types of deviant activity, which are not particularly unusual. Over-explanation is such that, at the extremes, any one process by itself could explain initiating drug use or offending. For example, a person with low enough self-esteem may offend without any of the other processes.

The processes also go some way towards explaining which young people develop the most serious problems – those most at risk in terms of the processes – but they are not specific about some key developmental issues:

- They cannot readily identify which type of problem a young person develops – it could be criminality, drug dependence, an alcohol problem, a mental health problem, something else, or some combination of the preceding.
- Nor can they readily identify precisely which young people develop the most serious problems, such as becoming career criminals or drug dependent.
- They fail to consider the impact of deviant behaviours themselves on people's lives. In longitudinal studies behaviour is the best predictor of future behaviour. This is not a trivial finding, drug use tends to lead to more drug use and crime tends to lead to more crime. It is also likely that drug problems make offending worse and vice versa.

Intensity
Among people who do use drugs, more intense drug users tend to be more criminal. 'Intense' is a multidimensional construct that includes use of a wider range of substances, use of substances that are perceived to be more dangerous, more frequent use, binging on

substances and involvement in dealing in drugs. Focus on the most visible or dramatic substances in a pattern of intense use can falsely imply a biological causality, when there is probably only a strong behavioural association. Heroin and crack cocaine are most often blamed for offending in this way. The intensity-criminality relationship also appears to apply to people who are not dependent and/or do not use the dramatic drugs, but this has not been adequately studied.

The intensity-criminality relationship might be due to the processes listed above. Some young people can engage in substance use and offending at high levels, but this may be temporary and does not indicate that their substance use causes their offending, or requires treatment for dependence. Longitudinal studies of delinquency have identified that for many offenders there is a temporary period of one to two years involving intense delinquent behaviour (Elliott *et al.*, 1985). This typically occurs aged 14 to 16 and, for most, is followed by a reduction or cessation of offending. This period can include intense drug use, which may also reduce afterwards. However, drug use tends to increase across ages 14 to 20 (e.g. Fergusson and Horwood, 2000), so rather than actually reducing, drug use may only continue to increase as normal. The risk processes described above better predict an intense period than they predict development of career criminality or drug dependency problems. Being relatively rare makes these behaviour patterns more difficult to predict.

Dependence
Amongst people who are dependent on a drug or drugs, offending to pay for drugs is common, although other forms of economic activity also occur. For drug dependent people, drug use causes crime in this sense and measures to reduce dependent people's illicit drug use, notably substitute prescribing, tend to reduce their offending. It is unclear that people under 18 are commonly dependent on drugs in this way. Yet, they may steal or commit other crimes to get money for drugs, not because they are compelled to by dependence, but because drugs are amongst the relatively expensive things that they want and cannot afford otherwise. Also, because both behaviours can be parts of a period of intense delinquent activity, that often also includes a variety of other problematic and acting-out behaviours.

Moderating
People who try offending, usually as teenagers, generally stop offending again before they are 20. These days, people who try drugs, also as teenagers, probably increase drug (and alcohol) use into their early 20s. This suggests that for most people drugs and crime develop separately after they are initiated. Trying to prevent all young people from increasing drug use as they grow up in the interests of crime prevention misunderstands this. An extreme minority tend to escalate both behaviours and, for them, which causes which is a moot

point. The key to the whole drugs crime problem is to know how and why this extreme minority develop. Gateway Theory (e.g. Fergusson and Horwood, 2000) documents the rise in drug use across adolescence into adulthood, but this trend is often confused with a movement towards dependence and criminality that does not occur in most cases. For example, that almost everyone who tries heroin or cocaine has tried cannabis first does not imply that cannabis causes dependence on heroin or cocaine, which is different from trying them anyway.

Limitations of risk assessment

Risk factors can predict which people are more likely to try drugs and offending, and also which are most likely to go through an intense period of one or both behaviours. Where understanding falters is in understanding how and why some people discontinue delinquency, some become substance dependent and some merely increase their substance use experience, but avoid becoming dependent.

Limitations of past work

Past studies' relevance to the contemporary UK situation may be limited. First, some of these studies began in the 1950s or 1960s before drug abuse was widespread (e.g. Farrington, 1996). Second, most studies examine a wide range of developmental issues, so drug use and offending are recorded in less detail than a specialist might like. Third, even the more recent studies have not examined the problems under the same social conditions as exist today in the UK and most work has occurred in the US. One exception is the work of Howard Parker and colleagues (Aldridge *et al.*, 1999; Parker *et al.*, 1998), who have followed young drug users through adolescence into early adulthood. Using both qualitative and quantitative data, Parker and colleagues have reached different conclusions about risk factors for drug use in the UK, in particular relating to the notion of normalisation.

Normalisation

Parker *et al.* (1998) developed the idea that drug use has become 'normalised' amongst young people, which involves the cultural incorporation of drugs, drug use and drug users into their everyday lives. Normalisation is not to say that drug use is 'normal' but rather that most young people, even those who do not use drugs, know drug users, have been exposed to drugs and therefore accommodate drugs to an extent, whatever their personal values about them. Furthermore, normalisation involves the acceptance of a wider range of substances as alternative choices for intoxication or a 'buzz', including alcohol, tobacco and cannabis quite routinely, and other drugs occasionally. Contemporary youth use a wider range of substances more often and freely than past generations did; including Class A drugs traditionally thought to be addictive. Parker *et al.* (1998) amongst others have shown that these drugs can be used recreationally without leading downwards to dependence. Other pathways into and out of drug use exist.

Normalisation amongst young offenders?

YOT clients, as well as being offenders, are young people with normal activities and interests. Substance use will be amongst these and for some YOT clients there may be no particular link between substance use and offending, apart from their age and cultural accommodation of drug use. Apparent links will be exaggerated by adult concerns about the extensive use of alcohol, tobacco and drugs by young people, including those too young to purchase alcohol or tobacco legally. That is, drug use may be 'normalised' amongst young offenders as much as amongst young people in general (see Patton, 2002). This implies that at least some forms of substance use amongst young offenders should have decoupled from the classic 'risk factors', while offending and other forms of substance use may stay linked to them.

On the other hand, it may be that young offenders continue to use substances above the (now increased) rates found in the general population. These high rates of use combined with offending may continue to place some young offenders at risk of substance dependence, but perhaps the criteria or risk factors that do so have changed. For example, heroin or cocaine use or drug injecting used to be a risk factor for a drug dependent criminal career, but normalisation may have altered this.

Youth Lifestyles Survey

In the UK, the most recent and relevant survey is the Vulnerable Groups analysis of the Youth Lifestyles Survey (YLS) (Goulden and Sondhi, 2001). This included four groups of young people considered to be at high risk for drug use: young offenders; school truants and excludees; homeless and runaway young people, and young people living in drug using families. Data were analysed by self-reported offending. As usual, offenders reported drug use at many times the rate of non-offenders. Even YLS 'minor' offenders report higher prevalence of drug use than the nearest comparable (but somewhat older) British Crime Survey (BCS) (Ramsay *et al.*, 2001) age group, except for drugs with very low rates of reporting, notably heroin and crack cocaine. The pattern of substance use makes it superficially implausible that the drug use and offending association is simply due to drug dependence, for drugs that can be used recreationally predominate, such as cannabis and amphetamines.

The basic finding that drug use and offending continue to be associated is supported by analysis of the entire YLS sample (Flood-Page *et al.*, 2000). Young people were categorised according to whether they were 'serious and persistent offenders' (three or more offences admitted in the last 12 months, and/or at least one serious offence) or not. Of serious and persistent offenders aged 12 to 17, 38 per cent of males and 20 per cent of females admitted using drugs in the last 12 months, compared to seven per cent (males) and four per cent (females) of the rest of the cohort. Serious and persistent offenders were also more likely to report using heroin, methadone, cocaine or crack cocaine and users of these drugs were more likely to have committed property offences than were other drug users or non-users.

Unfortunately, in common with many recent UK surveys, the YLS did not report on frequency of use, or assess dependence, which makes it difficult to evaluate these findings. The lifetime or 12 month incidence of heroin, cocaine or Class A drug use are very weak indices of possible dependence, or intense use, particularly in the context of normalisation, when occasional use of these drugs has become more common. The survey reported here assessed both frequency of drug use and dependence, which will allow some inferences to be drawn about what patterns of behaviour place young offenders at risk of dependence.

The possibility of systematic under-reporting

As the YLS studied vulnerable groups, non-offenders in it may have been resilient survivors, who have resisted substance use and offending. However, as YLS is a self-report survey, 'non-offenders' must also include any people who were unwilling to admit to offending by self-report, as well as any who had for one reason or another forgotten offending or reattributed it as 'not really' offending. Similar under-reporting may help explain their low rates of drug use.

When arrestees' self-reported drug use is compared to their drug use as evidenced by urine testing, then it is clear that they under-report drug use. There is also evidence that under-reporting is systematically related to the perceived seriousness of the drug (Patton, 2002), so that cocaine, particularly crack, is most under-reported. The current survey did not independently confirm respondents' self-reports, but it will be important to be aware of issues of systematic under-reporting when interpreting the findings.

Contribution of the current study

The study reported here was designed to examine drug use by young offenders, including details of frequency of use[3] and assessing both licit and illicit substances. As drugs–crime relationships may have changed, the study also aimed to elicit information about a range of relevant socio-demographic and risk factors that might influence drug use and offending. While it is likely that normalisation has altered drugs-crime relationships, it is not clear *a priori* exactly what changes will be observed. However, the increase in drug prevalence has not seemingly been reflected in increased crime incidence.

---

3   That each drug is typically used in different quantities per session makes quantity-frequency assessment across a range of substances prohibitively complex.

2   Design and methods

Aims

The data presented here are from the first phase of a longitudinal study investigating substance use and offending amongst young people. The aim was to examine patterns of substance misuse amongst young offenders and identify relationships between substance misuse, offending, and personal and social risk factors.

Design

Data were collected using an extensive, structured questionnaire administered to participants on a one-to-one basis and completed under the guidance of a researcher. The original design was for 500 young people, aged between 14 and 17, from 10 YOTs across England and Wales to take part. In each geographical area, negotiation to access young people via the YOTs, recruitment of participants and data collection were undertaken by teams of local researchers, including academic researchers, independent contract researchers with expertise in the field, and volunteers associated with drug agencies.

The questionnaire

The questionnaire comprised primarily closed questions relating to the three areas of substance use, offending and risk and protective factors. Basic demographic data were also collected. Many of the questions are standard, but some were new and were piloted specifically for this project.

Questions on substance use

- Drug, alcohol, solvent and tobacco use. Use of 20 substances (plus three dummy drugs), ever, during last four weeks, age first used, and frequency of use over last 12 months. Frequency was categorised as follows for ease of completion: never, once, 2–5 days, 6–12 days, 13–24 days, 25–100 days and 101–365 days

- Assessment of Substance Misuse in Adolescents (ASMA) (Willner, 2000)
- Severity of Dependence Scales (SDS) (Gossop *et al.*, 1992), in relation to favourite drug and drug upon which respondent felt most dependent.

Questions on offending

- Self-reported offending (Graham and Bowling, 1996). Admission to 31 offences committed ever, and frequency in last 12 months, categorised as follows: never, once, 2–5 times, 6–20 times, more than 20 times
- Offences committed resulting in referral to YOT
- Number of previous convictions or warnings.

Questions on risk and protective factors

- Coping style, including escape drinking /drug use (Carver *et al.*, 1989)
- Self-esteem (Rosenberg, 1965)
- Family structure – who the young person lives with, and lived with for the longest period during childhood
- Perceived parenting style – measures of care, overprotection (Parker *et al.*, 1979) and control
- School affiliation
- Social networks
- Life problems and life events
- Social support.

Questions on demography and background

- Sex, age and ethnic group
- Qualifications obtained
- Education/employment status
- Type of order.

Pilot work

Pilot work was undertaken to inform procedures for accessing and recruiting participants, ethical considerations and development of the questionnaire (see Appendix A).

The main study

Accessing young people referred to YOTs

As stated, the original design was for a sample of 500 young offenders to take part. It was anticipated that young women would comprise a minimum of 20 per cent of the sample, and that the sample would approximately reflect the ethnic composition of the detected youth offending population of each area. It was also intended that half the sample would comprise those with an identified drug/alcohol problem (i.e. having been referred to an alcohol/drug project). Considerable challenges were faced in recruiting a sufficiently large sample for this study to be viable, however, relating to the YOTs, the young people and the fieldwork teams (see Appendix B for details). The final sample achieved is detailed in Chapter 3.

Completing the questionnaires

Participants met with a researcher on a one-to-one basis to complete the questionnaire. This approach provided opportunity for the researcher to ensure that questions were correctly understood, and assist if any difficulties or ambiguities arose. Given that many young offenders have a disrupted education, guidance of this nature seemed crucial. Previous research experience also indicates that this approach reduces superficial, insincere and incomplete recording.

Confidentiality and anonymity

Although most participants completed the questionnaire on YOT premises, all meetings were conducted in private. Participants were informed that the information they provided on the questionnaire was confidential to the research team, and would not be disclosed to anyone else – including anyone in the criminal justice system, drug and alcohol services or their families/carers. Some concern existed amongst the researchers about the potential for disclosure of additional information that would identify the participant (or others) as being 'at risk'. It was agreed that should such discussions develop, the young person would be informed that it would be necessary to convey concerns to the YOT. However, in no instance did this occur.

The longitudinal nature of the research meant that it was necessary to obtain contact information for all participants. Contact details were recorded and are stored separately from the questionnaire, the two being linked by an identity number.

Analysis

Data have been analysed using SPSS in four stages:
- descriptive statistics applied to all variables and, on basis of their distribution and other parameters, decisions made about the level at which each should be treated (i.e. nominal/binary, ordinal/interval)
- data reduction methods to develop appropriate scale/classification for substance use and another for offending
- correlation procedures to ascertain first-order relationships between risk variables, substance use and offending
- exploratory regression techniques to predict substance use and offending from risk factors with objective of developing useful predictive models.

3   Description of the study cohort

This chapter presents the demographic, background and offending profile of the cohort. Throughout the chapter variables were analysed by gender, age and ethnicity and where no such differences are reported, there were no such differences.

Demographic profile: sex, age and ethnicity

The final sample comprised 293 young people recruited from eleven YOTs across England and Wales. Eighty-one per cent (237) were male and 19 per cent (56) female. This compared to 85 per cent male YOT clients in the evaluations of the pilot YOTs (Holdaway *et al.*, 2001), but the sampling strategy targeted 20 per cent females. Only five people were younger than 14 and only one was aged 18. For subsequent analyses respondents were categorised into age groups 12–14 (18%, 53), 15 (23%, 67), 16 (29%, 86) and 17–18 (29%, 86) (one no answer).

The majority (83%, 242) of respondents were of white ethnicity (Table 3.1). Other ethnic origins were represented at higher rates than in the general population because three areas with high ethnic minority populations were deliberately included. In the different areas, the ethnic composition of the respondents approximately matched that of the local population of detected young offenders.

Table 3.1:   *Ethnic group*

Ethnicity	No.	%
Asian	12	4
Black	23	8
White	242	83
Mixed	13	4
No answer	3	1
Total	293	100

Background

Education and employment

Most young people do not take formal educational qualifications until they are age 16. Of the 172 respondents who were 16 or older, just 31 per cent (54) had a qualification (11 no answers). In addition, five per cent (3) of 15 year olds had a qualification. The greatest proportion of those who had obtained qualifications had obtained one or more GCSEs at grades D or E only (Table 3.2).

Table 3.2: Qualifications obtained

Qualification	No.	%
GCSE Grade D – E only	24	42
GCSE Grade A – C only	7	12
GCSE Grade A – C and D – E	5	9
NVQ level 1 only	5	9
NVQ level 1 and level 2	3	5
NVQ level 2 only	2	4
Other combinations[1]	11	19
Total	57	100

1   Each recorded by one respondent

Sixty-four per cent (186) of respondents were not in compulsory education (year 11 or below) at the time they completed the questionnaire (7 no answers). This included 36 per cent (43) of respondents aged 15 or younger.

Of the 186 respondents who were not in compulsory education, 68 per cent (126) had dropped out or been excluded before the age of 16; 43 per cent of the cohort. For the purpose of further analyses, a school-leaving summary was created (Table 3.3).

A summary of sets of circumstances (Appendix C) shows that 38 per cent (112) of respondents were in education at the time they completed the questionnaire, with a further 14 per cent (42) on a training scheme or apprenticeship. Six per cent (17) were in employment but not education, and 36 per cent (105) were not in education or employment.

Table 3.3:   School leaving summary

Schooling status	No.	%
Still at school in year 11 or below	98	33
Left/excluded before 16	127	44
Left age 16+	56	19
No answer	12	4
Total	293	100

Family structure

At the time they completed the questionnaire, most (70%, 204) young people were living in the home of their parents or step-parents. None of the young people was sleeping rough, although four recorded that they were homeless and stayed with friends. The greatest proportion of respondents (39%, 115) were living with their mother only, and a further five per cent (15) were living with their father only (Table 3.4). Thus 44 per cent of the cohort lived in lone parent households. In contrast, 22 per cent of households with dependent children comprised lone parents in the 2000 England and Wales census (http://www.statistics.gov.uk/STATBASE/Expodata/Spreadsheets/D3420.xls, accessed November 2002).

Table 3.4:   Who respondents live with at the moment

Person/people with whom live	No.	%
Both parents	45	15
Mother only	115	39
Father only	15	5
Mother and a stepfather	32	11
Father and a stepmother	6	2
Other relatives (not parents)	21	7
With a foster family/in care	22	8
With other residents (e.g. in supportive/sheltered housing)	12	4
With a partner (girlfriend/boyfriend)	7	2
On own/independently	10	3
Homeless and stay with friends or others when can	3	1
Homeless and sleeping rough	0	-
Other	3	1
No answer	2	1
Total	293	100

Participants were also asked with whom they had lived for the longest period while growing up. Nearly half (45%, 133) had lived for the longest period with their mother only; a further 31 per cent (91) grew up living mostly with both parents (Table 3.5). It will be seen in Chapter 7 that parenting arrangements had no impact on substance use or self-reported offending. Nor did parenting arrangements significantly affect perceived quality of parenting, or parental supervision, described in Chapter 4. This leaves the high frequency of single parent families noted, but why it should be so unexplained.

Table 3.5:   Who lived with for longest period while growing up

	No.	%
Both parents	91	31
Mother only	133	45
Father only	10	3
Mother and a stepfather	26	9
Father and a stepmother	1	*
Other relatives (not parents)	14	5
With a foster family/in care	11	4
Other	2	1
No answer	5	2
Total	293	100

*   Less than one per cent

Offending profile

Participants were asked to record, in their own words, the offences they had committed that resulted in their current referral to the YOT. Two hundred and seventy-seven answered; 196 detailed one offence, the remaining respondents listing between two and five. In total, 421 offences were detailed. The offences were grouped into nine main types (Table 3.6). Just over one-third (36%, 153) comprised some form of theft, and five per cent (19) were drug related.

Table 3.6:   Type of offence resulting in referral to YOT

Type of offence	No.	%
Theft	153	36
Disorder	69	16
Motoring	66	16
Assault	62	15
Drug	19	5
Dissent from the criminal system	12	3
Sexual	8	2
Fraud	7	2
Other	25	6
Total	421	100

Analysis by individual using the nine main groupings revealed that nearly one-third (30%, 88) of respondents had been convicted of theft-related crimes only, and that this was the case for 48 per cent (27) of women (Table 3.7).

Table 3.7:   Type of offence resulting in referral to YOT by individual

Combinations of type of offence	Men		Women		All respondents	
	No.	%	No.	%	No.	%
Theft only	61	26	27	48	88	30
Motoring only	36	15	4	7	40	14
Disorder only	25	11	3	5	28	10
Assault only	19	8	4	7	23	8
Other only	13	6	0	-	13	5
Theft & Motoring	8	3	0	-	8	3
Disorder & Assault	5	2	3	5	8	3
Theft & Disorder	7	3	0	-	7	2
Theft & Assault	5	2	2	4	7	2
Sexual only	7	3	0	-	7	2
Theft, Disorder & Assault	4	2	2	4	6	2
Drug only	5	2	1	2	6	2
Other combinations[1]	30	13	5	9	35	12
No answer	12	5	5	9	17	6
Total	237	100	56	100	293	100

1   Each identified by one per cent or fewer respondents

The majority (84%, 246) of the young people had had one or more warnings (28 no answers); mean number of warnings=3.4 (sd=4.3). Seventy-nine per cent (232) of participants had had one or more previous convictions (32 no answers) and 179 recorded the number they had obtained; mean=6.4 (sd=11.4).

Figure 3.1 shows the main elements of the disposals made on the young offenders. It can be seen that the most common elements were supervision, surveillance or curfew (36%), action plans (14%) and reparation or community service (12%). There were very few final warnings in this cohort, because of the sampling method used. Supervision orders ranged from one month to 36 months in length, but were most frequently one year (34%, 30), while action plans ranged from one month to 28 months in length, but were most frequently three months (74%, 26).

Figure 3.1: *Frequency of main elements of disposals in the cohort*

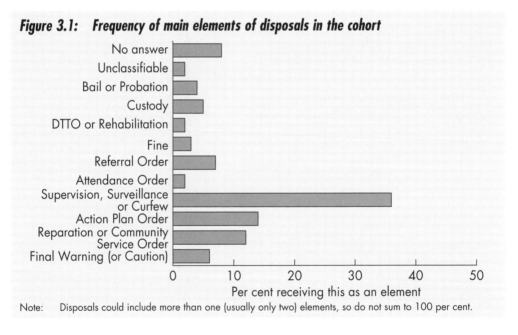

Note: Disposals could include more than one (usually only two) elements, so do not sum to 100 per cent.

These data demonstrate that the sample recruited for this research should not be considered representative of all young offenders. They over-represent those with longer offending histories who were more involved with the YOT in some sense. The preponderance of supervision, surveillance and curfew orders is also striking.

Summary of demographic, background and offending profile

- The study group comprised predominantly white males aged 15 and 16.
- Women are represented in approximately the same proportion as in YOTs generally; ethnic minority groups are over-represented due to the sampling method.
- Many had been excluded or had dropped out from school before age 16, and most left school without qualifications; a considerable proportion was in neither education nor employment.
- The most common past and current family circumstance was for young people to live with their mother only; this was the case for a greater proportion of this cohort than in the general population.
- The sample is not representative of all young offenders, over-representing those with longer offending histories and who had greater involvement with the YOT.

4   Personal traits and experiences

Personal traits investigated were coping mechanisms, self-esteem, school affiliation and sociability. Plans and expectations for the future were also explored. Experiences investigated were parenting, and life events and problems. These variables were included because they may influence substance use and offending. This chapter reports differences between sexes, age groups and ethnic groups on these variables. Where differences are not mentioned there were none.

Personal traits

Coping mechanisms

Coping style, including escape drinking/drug use, was investigated with questions devised by Carver *et al.* (1989), since substance misuse may be a dysfunctional means of coping with life problems. The items used are those most commonly endorsed according to Williams (1998). Table 4.1 shows coping mechanisms, ordered by the percentages of people who reported using them. It can be seen that over a third of the cohort reported using alcohol or drugs 'more than a little' to escape from problems. It is also noteworthy that for each coping mechanism listed the majority of respondents used it only a little, if at all.

Table 4.1:   Coping mechanisms (items in italics are negative methods)

	Not at all %	A little bit %	More than a little[1] %
I do something about it	17	37	45
I learn something from the experience	26	30	42
I drink alcohol or take drugs,			
in order to think about it less	38	20	39
I talk to someone I know about how I feel	41	26	31
I make sure not to make matters			
worse by acting too soon	41	27	30
I make fun of the situation	45	30	23
I pretend that it hasn't really happened	46	32	20
I make a plan	61	22	16
I seek God's help	81	10	7

Notes: 1 Comprised collapsed categories 'a medium amount' and 'a lot'.
          Between 4 and 8 respondents did not provide an answer for each item.

Self-esteem

Self-esteem was investigated using Rosenberg's (1965) 10-item self-esteem inventory. Scores of more than three suggest low self-esteem. Women had lower self-esteem than men and 38 per cent of women scored more than three, compared with 14 per cent of men.

School affiliation

School affiliation was investigated using three positively worded items and one negatively worded (Table 4.2). A school affiliation score for each individual was calculated out of a possible total of 20 (4 items rated 1 to 5); the higher the score the greater the level of school affiliation. The mean score was 10.2 (sd=3.8). There was a trend for white respondents to be least affiliated with schooland Asian groups to be most affiliated (Asian=12.2, Black=11.9, White=9.9, Mixed=11.3; p<0.05). However, post hoc tests indicated that this effect was not large enough for any of the groups to differ significantly from the others. It can be seen in Table 4.2 that only a minority of the cohort were positive about school and two-thirds agreed that they played truant a lot.

Table 4.2:   School affiliation (item in italics is negatively worded)

When at school I...	Agree %	Neutral %	Disagree %
enjoy(ed) it	27	21	51
do/did well	29	28	41
feel/felt my school work was important	34	14	50
play(ed) truant a lot	*67*	*10*	*22*

Notes: Between 3 and 6 respondents did not provide an answer for each item
Agree is combination of strongly agree and agree. Disagree is combination of strongly disagree and disagree.

Sociability

People who are out and about seeing other people more often are more likely to offend, more likely to be detected offending and more likely to self-report drug use. All three are due to increased opportunity, so it is important to assess sociability as a potential confounding variable linking drug use and crime.

Participants were asked about the frequency with which they interacted with friends in different ways during a normal week. More than two-thirds visited with friends (76%, 223), met friends outside (76%, 224) and/or phoned their friends (68%, 200) most or every day.

Other forms of interaction were less common. An overall 'social contact score' for each individual was calculated, a higher score indicating greater levels of contact. Out of a possible total of 35 (7 items rated 1 to 5) the mean score was 21.2 (sd=4.8). Perhaps surprisingly, there were no differences by age, sex or ethnicity.

The cohort tended to socialise most frequently locally. Whereas 44 per cent (129) shopped or hung out in their local town 2 to 4 times a week or more, only 15 per cent (44) travelled this frequently to a town further away to do so. Furthermore, 42 per cent (123) of respondents recorded that they never travelled to a town further away than their local town to shop or hang out, and 56 per cent (164) that they never travelled to a town further away than their local town to go out at night.

In terms of more personal relationships, participants were asked how many people they had dated, gone out with, or had a relationship with in the past 12 months; the mean response was five (sd=4). Men recorded having had slightly more partners than women (5 vs. 4, $p < 0.05$). The median length of relationship was one or two months.

Plans and expectations for the future

It is difficult to predict which young offenders will quit or moderate offending and/or drug use. One type of difference between people that may be important is how they view themselves. Not only general self-esteem, described above, but whether they regard their current delinquency as temporary or not. Therefore, expectations for the future were briefly assessed, both positive expectations – educational and earning aspirations – and expecting to be in trouble with the law again. Aspirations for marriage and children were not assessed, because serial monogamy has greatly diversified normal aspirations for this aspect of life (Parker et al., 1998).

Planned qualifications

Sixty-nine per cent (201) of respondents planned to obtain one or more qualifications between the time they completed the questionnaire and when they were 25 (15 no answers). Most planned to obtain GCSEs, A levels or NVQs; only seven per cent planned to obtain a professional qualification and 12 per cent currently planned to go to university.

Plans for earning

Only 35 per cent of respondents expected to be earning above the 2002 average household income (£446 per week, CACI, Wealth of the Nation, 2002) by the time they were 25. Thirty per cent expected to be earning £151–£300 per week, which is at the lower end of the current incomes (Table 4.3). Those of Asian origin hoped to have the highest earnings, while those of mixed origin anticipated the lowest (p=.002).

Table 4.3:   Expected earnings at age 25

Expected earnings	No.	%
Less than £150 per week	33	11
£151 – £300 per week	88	30
£301 – £450 per week	72	25
£451 – £600 per week	28	10
£601 – £750 per week	10	3
£751 – £1,000 per week	14	5
More than £1,000 per week	32	11
No answer	16	6
Total	293	100

Expectations of being in further trouble by the age of 25

Table 4.4 shows that, when asked to rate how likely these things were, substantial minorities of the cohort thought it likely that they would be in trouble with the law again and that they would have a prison sentence by the time they were 25.

Table 4.4:   Expectations of being in further trouble by the age of 25

	Likely %	Maybe %	Unlikely %
Likelihood of being in trouble with the law again by the time 25	31	15	43
Likelihood of having a prison sentence by the time 25	23	22	53

Notes: 4 respondents did not provide an answer for each item
'Likely' includes 'Very Likely'; 'Unlikely' includes 'Very Unlikely'

Experiences

Parenting

Respondents' views of their parents'[4] parenting style were assessed using four items from The Parental Bonding Instrument (Parker *et al.*, 1979) and an additional item investigating the way in which drugs were discussed (Table 4.5). Respondents were generally positive about their parenting, with over half agreeing with the positive statements and less than 20 per cent agreeing that their parents were emotionally cold. However, less than half agreed that drugs had been discussed in a helpful way and more than half felt that parents had tried to control everything they did.

Table 4.5: *Perceived parenting style (items in italics are negatively worded)*

In the home where I grew up, my parents or other adults looking after me…	Agree or strongly agree %
1. Appeared to understand my problems and worries	56
2. Let me decide things for myself	55
3. Discussed drugs with me in a way I found helpful	41
4. Seemed emotionally cold to me	*18*
5. Tried to control everything I did	*55*

Note: Between 5 and 7 respondents did not provide an answer for each item.

An apparent contradiction emerges in that 55 per cent of respondents reported that their parents let them decide things for themselves, and 55 per cent recorded that their parents tried to control everything they did. This highlights a limitation of the instrument, in that some respondents commented that they were treated differently by their two parents and wanted to respond accordingly.

Items 1 and 4 are taken from the Care Scale of the instrument, and items 2 and 5 from the Overprotection Scale. Separate scores for each of these dimensions of parenting were therefore calculated (maximum score=10, higher scores indicate higher perceived levels of caring and overprotection). Mean scores were Care 7.2 (sd=2.0) and Overprotection 6.0 (sd=2.0). Those of Asian origin perceived their parents as more overprotective than did whites (Asian=7.67, White=5.90, $p<0.05$).

---

4   The term 'parents' includes other adults who looked after the respondent whilst growing up.

A further question investigated respondents' perception of parental control. Although 54 per cent (156) had parents who often or very often expected them to be in at a set time, less than one-half recorded that their parents often or very often knew where they were when they were out, or what they were doing, or who they were with (Table 4.6). It is important to note that these findings reflect the young people's perceptions of their parenting – their parents may have felt quite differently.

Table 4.6: *Perceived parental control*

In the home where I grew up, my parents or other adults looking after me...	Strongly agree or agree %	Neutral %	Strongly disagree or disagree %
knew where I was when I was out	30	27	38
knew what I was doing when I was out	21	27	50
knew who I was with when I was out	42	31	26
expected me to be in at a set time	54	23	22

Note: Between 4 and 10 respondents did not provide an answer for each item.

A perceived parental control score for each individual was calculated out of a possible total of 20 (4 items rated 1 to 5); the higher the score the greater the level of perceived parental control. The mean score was 12.2 (sd=3.8).

Life problems, events and support

Participants were asked about a list of life problems that might apply to them (Figure 4.1) and a list of more acute life events that they might have experienced during the previous two years (Figure 4.2). These two lists were designed to cover common major adolescent problems fairly comprehensively. Life problems are things that may have long term effects on adolescent development and hence remain relevant even if they began a long time ago, while life events are things whose effects are largest within two years of occurrence[5]. More than one-quarter (26%, 76) of respondents had experienced five or more of the life problems ever, although few patterns of combinations of problems emerged. The most frequently recorded combination of problems were having been excluded from school and parents having divorced or separated (8%, 24) and having been excluded from school, parents having divorced or separated and member of family having a criminal record (8%, 24).

---

5   Although life events may also have persistent effects.

Figure 4.1: *Life problems experienced ever*

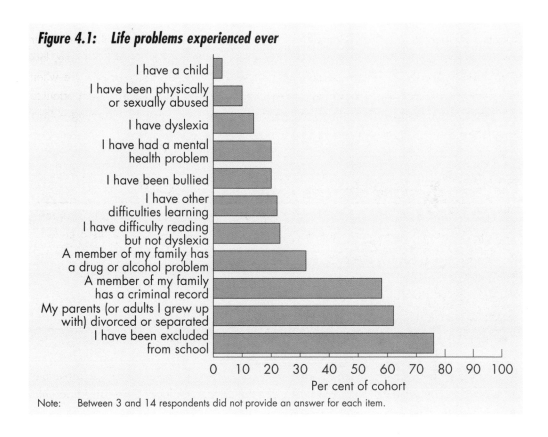

Note: Between 3 and 14 respondents did not provide an answer for each item.

In terms of events experienced during the previous two years (Figure 4.2, overleaf), most frequently identified were the death of a close friend or family member (54%, 158), having been depressed (43%, 125), having moved house or left home (40%, 116), and having broken up with a long-term boyfriend or girlfriend (37%, 108). One-third (33%) had been beaten up and nearly one-quarter (23%) had been a victim of theft or robbery.

This cohort was relatively unlikely to share feelings or problems with others. Under half would talk to parents (49%), friends (48%), siblings (46%), partners (41%) or other family members (40%). The most likely professional to talk to was a counsellor, which was rated as likely or very likely by 22 per cent. GPs, teachers and others were less likely. Also, 43 per cent reported that they were likely to keep their feeling or problems to themselves.

Summary of personal traits and experiences

- The cohort included a large minority, particularly of women, with low self-esteem. Collectively, they did not use many positive coping mechanisms and over a third used alcohol or drugs as escape coping.
- The majority of the cohort did not like school or get along well there.
- The cohort had low, but typical, aspirations for adult achievement, but many expected to get into trouble with the law again.
- The young people felt less positive about their parents discussing drugs than other aspects of parenting.
- The young people tended to see friends regularly, mostly close to home, and also dated regularly.
- Over 50 per cent of the cohort had experienced school exclusion, parental divorce or separation, a family member with a criminal record, and/or bereavement. Multiple problems and life events were common.
- Nearly one-quarter had been a victim of crime in the previous two years.
- Almost half the cohort would keep their feelings and problems to themselves.

Figure 4.2: *Life events experienced during the previous two years*

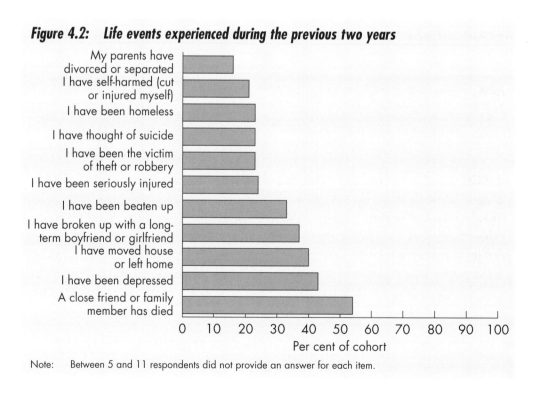

Note: Between 5 and 11 respondents did not provide an answer for each item.

5   Service use and service involvement

In health service research, extensive service use is an indicator of psychosocial problems and the same can be assumed here. In survey work with populations expected to be physically healthy (such as young offenders) 'extensive' is sometimes rather modestly defined as at least two service visits in a year[6]. As well as suggesting problems, some forms of service use may help, prevent or reduce offending or substance abuse, while lack of service use (where it might be appropriate) also provides information about unmet service needs for young offenders. For all these reasons, participants were asked how many times they had been in contact with a variety of support agencies during the previous two years.

The agency with which the greatest proportion of young people had been in contact most frequently was a GP; 33 per cent (97) had seen one more than three times (Table 5.1). More than one-half (54%, 157) of the young people had been to an accident and emergency (A&E) department for treatment on one or more occasions during this period and 11 per cent had been more than three times. Only a minority had seen a counsellor (20%, 59) or visited a drug or alcohol service (24%, 69). Just over one-half (51%, 149) had been visited by a social worker.

Table 5.1:   Contact with support agencies

In the past two years I have been...	Never		Once		Two or three times		More than three times	
	No.	%	No.	%	No.	%	No.	%
to a GP	66	23	39	13	86	29	97	33
to A&E for treatment	128	44	78	27	47	16	32	11
visited by a social worker	139	47	25	9	34	12	90	31
to hospital overnight or longer	188	64	59	20	19	9	14	5
to a drug or alcohol service	220	75	16	6	20	7	33	11
to counselling for a problem	229	78	15	5	10	3	34	12

Note: Between 4 and 8 respondents did not provide an answer for each item.

---

6   This definition excludes normal single visits for simple problems. The logic is that repeated GP or other service use is often an indicator of underlying psychosocial problems, even when the repeat visits are ostensibly for specific physical problems. This of course does not apply to people with chronic conditions routinely requiring repeat visits, but there will be relatively few of them in an adolescent cohort.

Participants were then asked whether they had received special help with a range of problems and behaviours (Table 5.2). The aspect with which the greatest proportion of respondents had received help was their offending behaviour (74%, 216), and over one-half (52%, 151) had received special help with their education.

Table 5.2: Special help received

	Had special help	
	No.	%
Offending behaviour	216	74
Education	151	52
Getting a job	127	43
Family problems	123	42
Drug or alcohol use	96	33
Worries and difficulties	89	30
Physical health problems	64	22
Mental health problems	49	17

Note: Between 19 and 40 respondents did not provide an answer for each item.

Only a minority of those who did not receive special help about each aspect recorded that they had needed some (Table 5.3). However, more than one-tenth of the cohort had received no special help with their education but felt they had needed some, and/or had received no special help with finding a job and felt they had needed some. Help with drug problems will be explored in more depth in Chapter 6.

Those who had received special help about each of the problems or behaviours were asked about the amount of such help received and its usefulness. In terms of the amount of help received, the only behaviour about which anything approaching one-half of respondents recorded they had received 'a lot' was offending (46%, 100). One-fifth or more of respondents recorded that they had received 'very little help' with education (20%, 30), mental health problems (29%, 14) and family problems (27%, 33), although it is important to note that data about the amount of help 'needed' was not obtained.

Table 5.3: *Special help needed*

	Number who did not have special help	Did not receive special help, but felt they needed some:	
		As percent of those not receiving help	As percent of entire cohort
Offending behaviour	60	17	3
Education	123	33	14
Getting a job	129	27	12
Family problems	130	10	4
Drug or alcohol use	162	10	6
Worries and difficulties	167	15	9
Physical health problems	190	4	2
Mental health problems	199	5	3

Note: Between 19 and 40 respondents did not provide an answer for each item.

Turning to the perceived usefulness of the help (Table 5.4), for all aspects except 'getting a job', 40 per cent - 50 per cent of those who received help rated it only as 'better than nothing' or 'no use at all'. Few respondents (less than 25% for all behaviours/problems) rated any of the help as 'very useful'. Sixty-one per cent (75) of respondents rated the help they received with getting a job as 'useful' or very useful'.

Table 5.4: *Perceived usefulness of help received*

	No.	Very useful		Useful		Better than nothing		No use at all	
		No.	%	No.	%	No.	%	No.	%
Offending behaviour	216	41	19	72	33	44	20	46	21
Education	151	36	24	45	30	33	22	30	20
Getting a job	127	28	22	47	37	22	17	17	13
Family problems	123	19	15	34	28	28	23	30	24
Drug or alcohol use	96	19	20	24	25	23	24	23	24
Worries and difficulties	89	10	11	33	37	18	20	20	23
Physical health problems	64	6	9	18	28	15	23	15	23
Mental health problems	49	5	10	13	27	12	15	13	27

Note: Between 6 and 13 respondents did not provide an answer for each item

Summary of service use

- GPs and Social Work were the most common services used.
- More than one-half of respondents had visited an A&E department during the previous two years.
- The pattern of service use implies high rates of psychosocial problems in the cohort.
- More than one-tenth of the cohort felt they needed special help with education and/or getting a job and had not received any.
- The quality of help received was generally felt to be low; over 40 per cent said it had been only better than nothing or no use at all – except for help with getting a job.

6   Offending and substance use

Offending

Self-reported offending ever, and frequency in last 12 months, were investigated in relation to 31 offences. The majority of the offences were taken from the British Crime Survey (BCS) (Graham and Bowling, 1996) with additional items exploring drug-related offences and soliciting. An instruction made it explicit that respondents should answer positively to an offence if they had *committed* it, irrespective of whether they were caught.

Offences ever committed

The five most frequently committed offences were wilful damage (82%, 240), shoplifting (80%, 235), fighting/disorder (71%, 208), buying stolen goods (70%, 205) and selling stolen goods (70%, 204) (Appendix D). To facilitate investigation of the combination of offences the young people had committed, the 31 offences were grouped into nine categories (Figure 6.1). The type of offence to which the greatest proportion of respondents admitted was theft (92%, 269). However, for all types of offence other than fraud and those of a sexual nature, more than one-half of respondents admitted to having committed them at some time.

Figure 6.1:   Types of offence committed ever

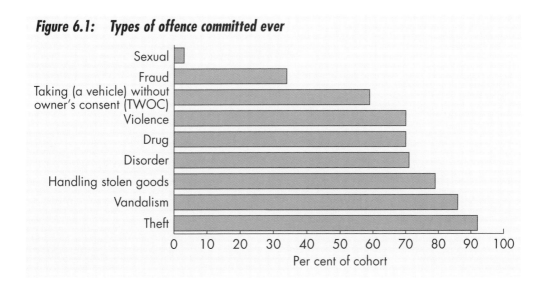

Despite the grouping of types of offences, however, analysis by individual revealed few clear patterns. Most respondents (61%, 179) admitted to committing six or more different types of offences, indicating that the cohort consisted of relatively experienced offenders.

Offences committed during last 12 months

Compared to lifetime offending, Table 6.1 shows a similar pattern of offences committed during the last 12 months. The four offences most commonly committed are the same in both cases: wilful damage (64%, 188), shoplifting (61%, 179), fighting/disorder (65%, 191) and selling stolen goods (60%, 176). The fifth most frequently recorded, however, was having bought drugs for other people (59%, 172), followed by buying stolen goods (58%, 169).

These six offences were those most frequently recorded for each of the sexes. Statistical differences existed between the sexes for seven offences: a greater proportion of men than women recorded having stolen a bicycle, motorbike and/or car, and stealing something out of a car. In contrast, a greater proportion of women had committed shoplifting offences, used a stolen cheque book or cash card to obtain cash and/or snatched a bag/purse. Nearly one-half (47%, 139) of respondents admitted to committing six or more different types of offence during this period.

Table 6.1:   Offences committed in last 12 months

Offence	Men (n=237) %	Women (n=56) %	All (n=293) %
Taken part in fighting or disorder in a group in a public place	66	63	65
Damaged or destroyed, purposely or recklessly, something belonging to someone else	64	64	64
Stolen anything from a shop, supermarket or department store*	58	75	61
Sold something that you knew, or believed at the time, was stolen	63	48	60
Bought drugs for other people	59	55	59
Bought something that you knew, or believed at the time, was stolen	58	55	58
Stolen anything out of or from a car**	54	29	50
Kept or carried large quantities of drugs	43	45	44
Taken away a car without the owner's permission, not intending to give it back*	46	30	43
Sold drugs to other people for money	42	43	42
Hurt someone with a knife, stick or other weapon	43	34	42

Table 6.1 (continued)

Offence	Men (n=237) %	Women (n=56) %	All (n=293) %
Sneaked into someone's garden or house or a building intending to steal something	41	32	39
Beaten up someone not belonging to your immediate family to such an extent that you think or know that medical help or a doctor was needed	40	36	39
Taken away a bicycle without the owner's permission, not intending to give it back**	44	18	39
Set fire, purposely or recklessly, to something not belonging to you	41	30	39
Taken away a motorbike or moped without the owner's permission, not intending to give it back**	42	16	37
Threatened someone with a weapon or with beating them up to get money or other valuables from them	32	32	32
Stolen anything worth more than £5, not mentioned already	30	20	28
Stolen money from a gas or electricity meter, public telephone, vending machine, video game or fruit machine	30	20	28
Stolen anything in school worth more than £5	21	23	22
Stolen anything from a place that you worked worth more than £5	17	13	16
Used a chequebook, credit card, cash-point card (ATM card) that you knew or believed at the time to be stolen to get money out of a bank account*	13	29	16
Beaten up someone in your immediate family to such an extent that you think or know that medical help or a doctor was needed	13	23	15
Snatched from someone a purse, bag or something else*	12	27	15
Pick-pocketed anything from anybody	11	14	12
Sold a chequebook, credit card, cash-point card (ATM card) belonging to you or someone else so that they could steal money from a bank account	8	13	9
Claimed social security benefits to which you knew that you were not entitled	5	7	6
Made false claim on an insurance policy	3	4	3
Solicited, that is, offered or invited sex in exchange for money	3	5	3
Made an incorrect tax return	2	4	2

Notes: Between 7 and 10 respondents did not provide an answer for each item
Sex differences *p<0.05; **p<0.005

In relation to frequency, Table 6.2 shows that, for most offences, the majority of those who had committed it during the last 12 months had done so on more than one occasion. For the three drug-related offences, more than one-third of those who committed these during the last 12 months did so more than 20 times.

Table 6.2:   Frequency of offences committed in last 12 months

Offence	No.	% committed in last 12 months			
		Once	2-5 times	6-20 times	>20 times
Taken part in fighting or disorder in a group in a public place	191	28	34	25	14
Damaged or destroyed, purposely or recklessly, something belonging to someone else	188	27	47	14	12
Stolen anything from a shop, supermarket or department store?	179	20	34	15	31
Sold something that you knew, or believed at the time, was stolen	176	17	34	26	23
Bought drugs for other people	172	13	27	24	37
Bought something that you knew, or believed at the time, was stolen	169	25	38	24	14
Stolen anything out of or from a car	145	28	45	14	14
Kept or carried large quantities of drugs	128	19	27	20	35
Taken away a car without the owner's permission, not intending to give it back	126	29	29	21	20
Sold drugs to other people for money	124	19	23	23	36
Hurt someone with a knife, stick or other weapon	122	46	40	9	5
Sneaked into someone's garden or house or a building intending to steal something	115	28	46	13	13
Beaten up someone not belonging to your immediate family to such an extent that you think or know that medical help or a doctor was needed	115	38	42	17	4
Taken away a bicycle without the owner's permission, not intending to give it back	114	35	41	16	8
Set fire, purposely or recklessly, to something not belonging to you	113	47	35	11	7
Taken away a motorbike or moped without the owner's permission, not intending to give it back	109	29	44	16	11

Table 6.2 (continued)

Offence	No.	% committed in last 12 months			
		Once	2-5 times	6-20 times	>20 times
Threatened someone with a weapon or with beating them up to get money or other valuables from them	94	38	40	16	5
Stolen anything worth more than £5, not mentioned already	83	41	36	13	10
Stolen money from a gas or electricity meter, public telephone, vending machine, video game or fruit machine	81	43	38	11	7
Stolen anything in school worth more than £5	63	37	33	18	13
Stolen anything from a place that you worked worth more than £5	48	40	33	13	15
Used a chequebook, credit card, cash-point card (ATM card) that you knew or believed at the time to be stolen to get money out of a bank account	47	53	34	11	2
Beaten up someone in your immediate family to such an extent that you think or know that medical help or a doctor was needed	44	55	39	5	2
Snatched from someone a purse, bag or something else	43	54	30	14	2
Pick-pocketed anything from anybody	35	51	31	11	6
Sold a chequebook, credit card, cash-point card (ATM card) belonging to you or someone else so that they could steal money from a bank account	27	48	37	15	-
Claimed more than £5 in expenses that you knew that you were not entitled to	22	55	18	9	18
Claimed social security benefits to which you knew that you were not entitled	16	44	50	6	-
Made false claim on an insurance policy	10	50	40	10	-
Solicited, that is, offered or invited sex in exchange for money	9	33	33	11	22
Made an incorrect tax return	6	16	67	-	17

To facilitate comparisons, a score for offending during the last 12 months was calculated by awarding each offence a value according to the frequency with which it was committed. No significant differences existed between the scores of men and women, between the different age groups or between those of different ethnic origins.

Substance use

Participants were asked to record their use of 20 substances (plus three dummy drugs) ever, frequency of use (in days) over last 12 months, use during last four weeks, and age first used. In addition, the questionnaire included an Assessment of Substance Misuse in Adolescents (ASMA) (Willner, 2000), and a Severity of Dependence Scale (Gossop *et al.*, 1992) in relation to favourite drug and drug upon which respondent felt most dependent.

Substance use ever

Participants were asked whether they had ever taken each of a list of 23 substances (including three dummy drugs: KTC, TAC and Wacks). The majority had taken alcohol (91%, 266), cannabis (86%, 252) and/or tobacco (85%, 249) (Table 6.3). Less than one-half of respondents had taken each of the other substances. Forty-four per cent (130) had taken ecstasy, 41 per cent (120) amphetamines, and 37 per cent (106) poppers. Of opiates and cocaine, 18 per cent (54) of respondents had taken crack cocaine and 11 per cent (33) heroin. Just three respondents claimed to have taken the dummy drug KTC, one to have taken TAC and none Wacks. While this indicates little over-reporting of substance use, under-reporting cannot be assessed.

Table 6.3:   Substances used ever

Substance	n=293 %
Alcohol	91
Cannabis (blow, draw, spliffs, hash, grass, ganja)	86
Tobacco (cigarettes)	85
Ecstasy (MDMA, MDA, 'E')	44
Amphetamines (crank, speed, wizz, sulph)	41
Poppers (rush, amyl nitrite, butyl nitrite, liquid gold)	37
Psilocybin mushrooms (magic mushrooms, mushies, 'shrooms')	29
Temazepam (wobblies, mazzies, jellies)	29
Solvents (such as glues, gases, aerosols, lighter fluid)	26
Cocaine (charlie, coke)	25
LSD (acid, trips)	25
Valium	21
Crack cocaine (rocks, stones)	18
Heroin (smack, scag, brown, powder, junk, H)	11
Methadone	8
Ketamine (green, special K, ketavet)	5
Codeine (DF118)	5
PCP (angel dust)	4
Steroids (body-building drugs)	4
Other opiates (such as opium, palfium)	3
KTC (hardcore drugs)	1
TAC	*
Wacks (vids, DHCA, DVDA)	-

Note: Between 2 and 11 respondents did not provide an answer for each item.

Table 6.4 shows the mean age at which those who had used each of the substances remembered first doing so. Initiation into substances followed a well-known progression in this cohort, despite their highly delinquent status: more legal substances first, other drugs next and the Class A drugs widely perceived to be addictive last. So, alcohol and tobacco were tried youngest, then cannabis just after. Solvents and 'poppers' (amyl nitrate and butyl nitrate) came next at 13, followed by the other illegal drugs at about 14. As has been found in other recent research, some illegal drugs are being tried a mean of about a year younger than 20 years ago, although the mean age of initiating substance use remains 11, usually with tobacco or alcohol. General population samples of young people tend to report drug-trying spread out over the age of 14 to 16. This cohort appears to have compressed drug trying so that they tended to have tried most drugs by 15. Forty-five per cent (133) of respondents recorded having used six substances or more in their lifetime.

Table 6.4: Mean age substance first taken

Substance	No. taken substance ever	Mean age first used
Alcohol	266	11.7 (sd=2.7)
Tobacco	249	11.7 (sd=7.1)
Cannabis	252	12.3 (sd=2.0)
Solvents	77	13.0 (sd=1.6)
Poppers	106	13.3 (sd=1.8)
Amphetamines	120	13.8 (sd=2.1)
Temazepam	86	14.0 (sd=1.8)
Psilocybin mushrooms	86	14.2 (sd=1.4)
Valium	60	14.2 (sd=1.7)
LSD	72	14.2 (sd=1.2)
Ecstasy	130	14.6 (sd=1.4)
Crack cocaine	54	14.8 (sd=1.5)
Heroin	33	14.8 (sd=1.3)
Cocaine	73	15.0 (sd=1.2)
Methadone	22	15.1 (sd=1.4)

Thirteen respondents, six male and seven female, recorded that they had injected drugs, most commonly heroin only. While this is a small number, the disproportionate number of women injectors is striking. The mean age at which these respondents started injecting drugs was 14.9 (sd=1.7). This group was compared to the rest of the cohort using t-tests and Fisher's exact test, as appropriate. All differences reported here are significant. Those who had injected drugs had lower self-esteem and lower perceived parental control. Most notable, however, are the differences in life events experienced. Offenders who had injected drugs had experienced more life problems than those who had not injected (4.4 vs. 3.4). Specifically, a greater proportion of those who had injected drugs had been bullied, physically/sexually abused, and/or had a family member with a drug/alcohol problem. In addition a comparatively large proportion of this group had a family member with a criminal record. Offenders who had injected drugs had also experienced more life events in the previous two years (6.8 vs. 3.6). Specifically, a greater proportion had experienced the death of a close friend/family member, became pregnant (or partner became pregnant), moved house/left home, became homeless, was physically/sexually abused, thought of suicide, self-harmed, had an eating disorder, were depressed, and/or had another mental health problem. Drug injecting in this cohort clearly remains an indicator of potentially severe problems.

Substance use during the last 12 months

Table 6.5 details patterns of recent substance use in this cohort, while Figures 6.2 and 6.3 illustrate key points. Figure 6.2 begins by showing use in the last four weeks. It can be seen that for the three substances most frequently recorded as having been taken ever (alcohol, cannabis and tobacco), 70 per cent or more of those who had taken them ever had also taken the substance during the last four weeks. In addition, for each of these substances, 50 per cent or more of respondents had used the substance on between 25 and 365 days in the last 12 months. Figure 6.3 shows use in the previous 12 months. It can be seen that over 50 per cent of users of tobacco, cannabis and also heroin had used these drugs over 100 days in the previous 12 months, while only about a quarter of alcohol users had drunk alcohol this often (equivalent to over 2 days per week if the pattern was regular).

Figure 6.2: **Recent and lifetime drug use compared**

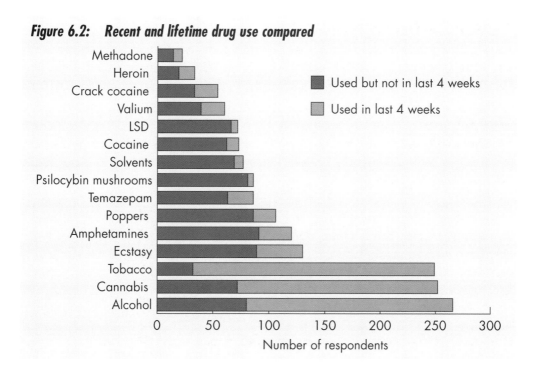

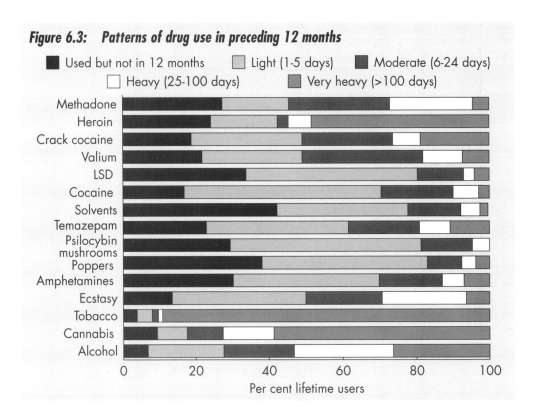

Figure 6.3: Patterns of drug use in preceding 12 months

Use of Ecstasy, amphetamine and poppers reveals a slightly different pattern (see Table 6.5). About one-third (32%, 41) of those who had ever used ecstasy had also used it in the last four weeks, and nearly one-half (48%, 63) had either not taken it at all during the last 12 months (28%, 7) or had taken it on only between one and five days. Less than one-quarter of those who had ever used amphetamines and poppers had also used them in the last four weeks. The majority of those who had taken poppers had either not taken them at all during the last 12 months or had taken them on only between one and five days. Frequency of amphetamine use was slightly higher, with 67 per cent (81) having taken this never or on just between one and five days in the last 12 months.

For heroin and crack cocaine, about 40 per cent of those who had ever taken these drugs had also taken them during the last four weeks (crack cocaine 39%, 21; heroin 42%, 14). However, a greater proportion of those using heroin were 'heavier users' than of those using crack cocaine (55%, 18 vs. 26%, 14).

Table 6.5: Patterns of substance use

| Substance | Taken ever | | Taken in last 4 weeks | | Never in last 12 months | | Frequency taken in last 12 months | | | | | |
| | | | | | | | Lighter 1-5 days | | Moderate 6-24 days | | Heavier 25-365 days | |
	No.	% of cohort	No.	% of ever used	No.	% of ever used	No.	% ever used	No.	% ever used	No.	% ever used
Alcohol	266	91	186	70	17	6	52	20	48	18	133	50
Cannabis	252	86	180	71	23	9	20	8	24	10	178	71
Tobacco	249	85	217	86	9	4	10	4	4	2	216	87
Ecstasy	130	44	41	32	17	13	46	35	26	20	37	28
Amphetamines	120	41	29	24	35	29	46	38	20	17	15	13
Poppers	106	37	20	19	40	38	47	44	10	9	8	8
Psilocybin mushrooms	86	29	5	6	25	29	44	51	12	14	4	5
Temazepam	86	29	23	27	19	22	32	37	16	19	16	19
Solvents	77	26	8	10	32	42	27	35	11	14	6	8
Cocaine	73	25	11	15	12	16	38	52	14	19	7	10
LSD	72	25	6	8	24	33	33	46	9	13	5	7
Valium	60	21	21	36	12	20	15	25	18	30	10	17
Crack cocaine	54	18	21	39	10	19	16	30	13	24	14	26
Heroin	33	11	14	42	8	24	6	18	1	3	18	55
Methadone	22	8	8	36	6	27	4	18	6	27	6	27

45

Comparisons with the Youth Lifestyles Survey (YLS) and the British Crime Survey (BCS) 2000
Data from the current study about lifetime and 12 months use of drugs were compared with those from the YLS and BCS 2000 (16-29) data. The 16 to 29 age range was chosen for comparison because it is a widely published sub-sample of the BCS and because a truly age-matched comparison would use 16 to 17 year-olds only, limiting the sample size in both surveys.

According to the offending categories used in the YLS, 88 per cent of the current cohort were 'serious' offenders, leaving too few 'minor' or 'non' offenders to compare. Figure 6.4 compares the lifetime drug use of serious offenders in the two samples and Figure 6.5 compares use in the past 12 months. It can be seen that prevalence of drug use in the present young offender cohort far exceeds prevalence in the YLS serious offenders.

Figure 6.4: Lifetime drug use by serious offenders: comparison of YLS and current study

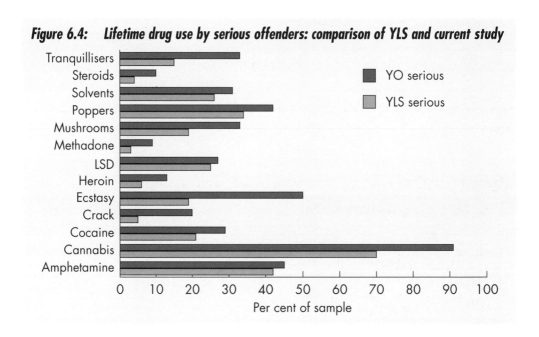

Figure 6.5: Drug use in last 12 months by serious offenders: comparison of YLS and current study

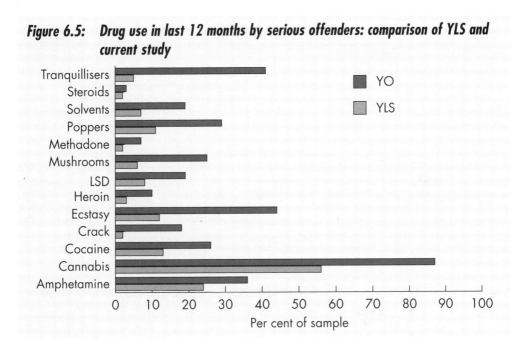

Figure 6.6 compares the lifetime drug use of the entire young offenders' cohort with the figures for ages 16 to 29 in the BCS. Figure 6.7 makes the same comparison with use in the past 12 months.

Figure 6.6: Lifetime drug use: comparison of BCS and current study

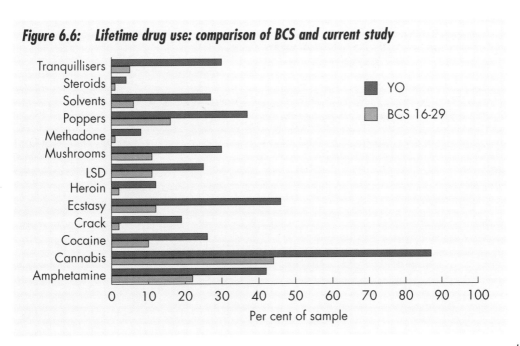

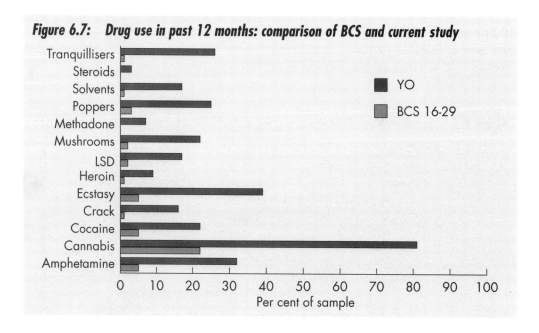

Figure 6.7: Drug use in past 12 months: comparison of BCS and current study

Despite the fact that the young offenders in the current study were aged 12 to 18, lifetime drug use prevalence is at least twice that of the BCS sample for all drugs, and the difference is even more marked for 12 month prevalence. It is important to be mindful of Patton's (2002) evidence that recent drug use is under-reported more than lifetime use and that people without a 'drug identity' – e.g. the general population – are more likely to deny drug use. Thus BCS 12 month figures may be under-reported relative to the current study.

Classifying offending for analysis of substance use

As described above, most people in the current study were serious offenders. This confirms that first time offenders and 'one-off' or experimental offenders were under-represented, because final warning orders were under-represented. For further analysis, a new classification of offending was therefore created using cluster analysis techniques[7]. This specified three groups, separable primarily in terms of frequency of offending. Figures 6.8 and 6.9 show the lifetime and past 12 month prevalence of drug use by these three groups. It can be seen that drug use prevalence was highest amongst the most frequent offenders, lower in medium offenders and lowest in the less frequent offenders. The only exceptions were cannabis, where prevalence amongst medium and frequent offenders was almost at

---

7   Using K-means cluster analysis specifying three groups, including frequency of all offences during the previous 12 months

100 per cent, and heroin, which was more prevalent amongst medium frequency offenders than amongst high frequency. This result is probably due to sampling error – there being relatively few heroin users.

Figure 6.8:   Lifetime drug use: frequent, medium and low offenders in the current study

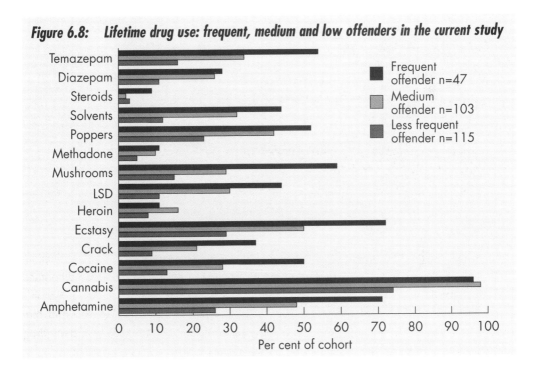

Three points should be noted. First, substance use in the present survey is considerably more prevalent than in either the YLS or the BCS. This is due in part to the present survey being of detected offenders, engaged with the YOT. In addition, the more intensive research method was designed to reduce under-reporting and may have succeeded, although there is no way of ascertaining this. Second, more frequent offending is associated with more prevalent drug use. Third, a larger proportion of more frequent offenders use all drugs, with no trend for them to use different drugs.

Figure 6.9: Drug use in last 12 months: frequent, medium and low offenders in the current study

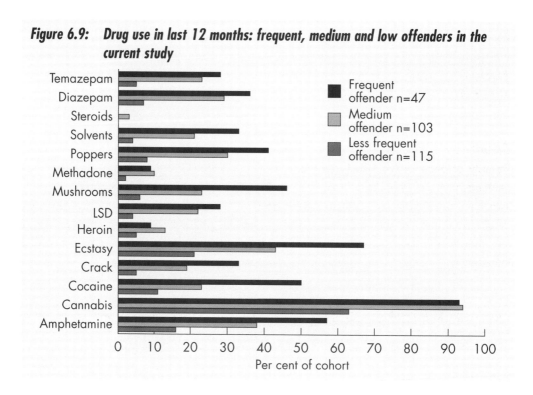

Predicting a substance misuse problem

Assessment of Substance Misuse in Adolescents

The Assessment of Substance Misuse in Adolescents (ASMA) (Willner, 2000) was used to identify those young offenders with a substance misuse problem (Appendix E) (n=245). ASMA has been validated against various diagnostic criteria, including DSM-IV diagnoses of substance abuse, or dependence, but the term 'drug problem' is preferred because of the difficulties of making a clear diagnosis of abuse or dependence in people with relatively brief careers of substance use. In reporting the results, figures in brackets show the equivalent percentages of 4,544 11 to 16-year-old school children (Willner, 2000).

Using the recommended cut-offs for ASMA, 65 per cent (92.2%) were classified as at low risk of drug problems, 20 per cent (6.4%) at medium risk and 15 per cent (1.4%) at high risk. Caution should be exercised in directly comparing the current study with Willner (2000) because the latter involved slightly younger people and excluded truants and those excluded from school. Nonetheless, a ten-fold higher prevalence of people at high risk for drug problems is dramatic. On the other hand, given the very high prevalence of drug use in this cohort, a relatively small proportion of respondents emerged as being at risk of problems.

Sixty respondents (51 men and 9 women) recorded that they had deliberately given up one or more drugs during the previous three months. These respondents therefore also completed the ASMA for the period immediately before they gave up the drug(s). No significant difference existed in the scores of these respondents before and after they gave up the drug(s).

Severity of dependence

Severity of dependence was investigated, in relation to favourite drug and drug to which respondents felt most addicted, using a scale devised and validated by Gossop *et al.* (1992). Two hundred and thirty-eight respondents had a 'favourite' drug, 231 of whom provided details. Most commonly identified was cannabis (Table 6.6). Although a greater proportion of men than women recorded cannabis as their favourite, and a greater proportion of women than men recorded alcohol, this difference did not reach statistical significance.

Table 6.6: *Percentages giving different substances as their 'favourite drug'*

Substance	n=231 %
Cannabis	64
Alcohol	23
Ecstasy	4
Heroin	4
Tobacco	2
Amphetamines	1
Cocaine	1
Crack cocaine	1
Temazepam	1

The Severity of Dependence Scale indicated that the majority of respondents had few concerns about being dependent upon their favourite drug. The 60 respondents who recorded that they had deliberately given up one or more drugs during the previous three months were also asked to complete the question on dependence on a favourite drug for the period immediately before they gave up the drug(s). Forty stated that they had had a favourite drug at this time, but overall, the findings suggest that diagnosable substance dependence was not a common problem amongst this cohort, despite extensive substance misuse that was related to offending. Problem drug use, as assessed with ASMA, is a better form of assessment in this age group.

Patterns of substance use and referral to a drug/alcohol project

Twenty-five per cent (74) of respondents had been referred to a drug/alcohol project while on their current order (15 no answers). Of these, three recorded having taken alcohol, cannabis and tobacco only, two alcohol and tobacco only, two cannabis only, and one alcohol and cannabis only. The remaining respondents recorded virtually unique combinations of between three and 14 substances. Of the 54 respondents who had ever used crack cocaine, 54 per cent (29) had been referred to a drug/alcohol project (1 no answer), and of the 33 who recorded they had ever used heroin, 58 per cent (19) had been referred (1 no answer). This will be explored further below. Table 6.7 shows referral by ASMA scores. It can be seen that more high risk users were referred than medium or low risk users, but that only about half the high risk group were referred to a drug or alcohol service. Slightly more of this high risk group had received some sort of help with a drug problem during the past two years. Unfortunately, the majority who received help did not feel that it was useful. This suggests that there is a considerable gap between current service provision for young offenders and their service needs.

Table 6.7: **Percentage of substance users referred to drug/alcohol projects and valuing help received with drug/alcohol problems by risk groups (ASMA score)**

	High risk (n=35)	Medium risk (n=47)	Low risk (n=151)
Referred to drug/alcohol project while on current order	51	38	19
Received at least 'some' help with drug problem during past two years	60	37	31
Felt help received was useful or very useful	36	48	36
(n=number who responded to this question)	(n=22)	(n=23)	(n=41)

It is not possible to determine from the current study why some of those using drugs are not referred to a drug/alcohol programme. A number of differences did however emerge between those who were referred and those who were not. In addition to their ASMA score, they had experienced more lifetime events ever (p<.05) and in the last two years (p<.01). No association existed, however, between offending score in the last two years and referral to the service.

Looking at the patterns of drug use by different ASMA levels, a potential difficulty for assessment and referral is that there were few marked differences in the drugs used or the frequency of their use between high, medium and low risk users. The exception was that 25 per cent of the high risk group had used heroin more than 100 days in the past year, compared to under three per cent of the lower risk groups. In this cohort who were young, delinquent and frequent users of a wide range of drugs, potential problems are likely to be to do with motives for and habits of drug use, not with which particular substances are used, and how often.

Perceptions of the association between substance use and offending

In addition to the proposed analyses to explore associations between offending and substance use (see Chapter 7), the study investigated participants' own perceptions of whether any such association existed; 269 answered. As can be seen in Table 6.8, over one-half agreed that alcohol or drugs had been associated with getting upset or angry, leading to offending, and 44 per cent recorded that they sometimes committed crimes in order to get money for drugs or alcohol. As discussed in Chapter 1, these links could be due to a period of intense behaviour – where offending and substance use are principally symptoms of underlying distress – or to developing substance problems.

Table 6.8: *Perceived relationship between substance use and offending*

Statement about substance use and offending	% agree or strongly agree n=269
When I have been high on alcohol or drugs I have sometimes got upset or angry and got in a fight	58
When I have been high on alcohol or drugs I have sometimes got upset or angry and smashed or destroyed things	55
I have sometimes got so high on alcohol or drugs that I didn't care what happened	52
If I happen to have had more money after committing a crime, then I may have drunk more or taken drugs more	50
Sometimes I have committed crimes in order to get money for drugs or alcohol	44
There is a relationship between taking drugs/alcohol and crimes I have committed	41
Sometimes I have taken alcohol or drugs to get the courage to commit crimes	25

Note: Between 1 and 5 respondents did not provide an answer for each item

Summary of offending and substance use

- The cohort was highly delinquent; most had committed at least six different types of offence.
- The only types of offence reported by a minority of the cohort in their lifetime were fraud and sex offences.
- More than 20 per cent of the cohort reported having committed the following offences more than 20 times: shoplifting, selling stolen goods, taking car without consent, buying drugs, keeping or carrying large quantities of drugs, selling drugs.
- Substance use was very prevalent in this cohort; considerably higher than reported in the Youth Lifestyles Survey and British Crime Survey 2000.
- Cannabis use was as prevalent as tobacco (86% vs. 85%) and almost as prevalent as alcohol (91%), being almost twice as common as any other drug.
- A range of drugs had been used by between 20 per cent and 44 per cent of the cohort; the presence of cocaine, temazepam and valium among these relatively prevalent drugs is of concern.
- Under 20 per cent of the cohort had used crack cocaine, opiates and some other rare drugs.
- Tobacco was the substance most likely to be used more than 25 days in the year, but alcohol, cannabis, ecstasy, crack cocaine, heroin and methadone had also been used this frequently by more than 20 per cent of those who had ever used them (although the numbers using were small for heroin, crack cocaine and methadone).
- Most illegal drugs were not first used until about 14, except cannabis, which is now on average used just after alcohol and tobacco at age 12. All illegal drugs had been tried by age 15.
- The small number of drug injectors in the cohort (n=13) differed from the remainder in being disproportionately women, in having experienced more life problems and events, having lower self-esteem and having experienced less parental control.
- Eighty-one per cent had a favourite drug, most commonly alcohol or cannabis.
- Although there was a high prevalence of use, few of the cohort reported dependence and only 15 per cent were rated (by ASMA) as at high risk of substance abuse problems. However, this is a ten-fold increase in risk compared to a school sample of young people.
- Users with more problematic use (assessed by ASMA) were more likely to have been referred to a drug service and/or received other help.
- Only a minority of those who received help felt it had been useful.
- Forty per cent or more of the cohort felt there was some relationship between their substance use and their offending.

7   Predicting substance use and offending

While the association between substance use and crime is well known, the underlying causes of this association are complex and controversial. As discussed in Chapter 1, prior to normalisation – in the 1980s – there were two main possible relationships between drug use and offending, as well as a variety of confounding and partially confounding factors:

1) Drug users tended to offend more than non-users, as part of a transitory adolescent delinquency involving both behaviours that may be more or less intense, even if it is temporary.

2) Those dependent upon heroin and, later in the UK, cocaine tended to offend more than those who did not use those drugs regularly and were not dependent on them. These relationships applied both in adults and in adolescents (see Hammersley *et al.*, 1989; 1990 for review).

One likely result of the subsequent normalisation of drug use is that relationships between drugs and offending may have changed. This chapter examines these relationships by first establishing what patterns of offending and what patterns of substance use exist in this study group, then looking at how different patterns relate together, and finally considering any other factors that may contribute to these relationships.

Preparatory analyses

A single index of offending frequency

The frequencies of different offences committed over the past 12 months were significantly correlated with each other. Factor analysis[8] indicated that there was one large offending factor that accounted for 29 per cent of offending variance and that a single factor solution was most appropriate[9]. A single frequency of offending was therefore created by adding together the number of different offences committed during the past 12 months. The distribution of this variable was skewed, so an index of offending was produced through log transformation. The raw frequency of offending in the last 12 months is also shown where relevant.

---

8   Exploratory principal components factor analysis.
9   The next factor accounted for only 6 per cent of variance and the scree plot then sloped gradually.

Three factors for substance use frequency

Factor analysis[10] was also conducted on the frequencies of substances used in the past 12 months (drugs used by very few people and fictional substances were excluded). Factors are tendencies within people, not separate sub-groups of people. The results of the factor analysis are summarised in Appendix F. The first factor accounted for 36 per cent of the variance in substance use, and use of all substances except tobacco loaded positively on this factor; it can therefore be described as a general tendency towards stimulant and polydrug use, with respondents using substances more or less frequently. Factor two accounted for a further 14 per cent of variance. Heroin and methadone loaded most highly on this factor, crack cocaine and valium also loaded positively, while alcohol and cannabis loaded negatively. This factor can therefore be described as a tendency toward use of opiates and other drugs perceived to be serious or addictive. Factor three accounted for an additional nine per cent of variance and loaded positively with tobacco, cannabis and alcohol, while poppers loaded negatively. This can therefore be described as a tendency to use more socially accepted substances. Together these three factors accounted for 59 per cent of the variance in substance use over the previous 12 months. The three factors or tendencies are not independent as some drugs load on more than one factor, but they form a reasonably comprehensive, sensible and brief way of summarising substance use. The decision was made to use the factor scores, along with the ASMA scores, as the primary measures of substance use for multivariate analysis.

Correlations between substance use and offending

Table 7.1 shows the correlations between the measures of substance use (factor scores and ASMA scores) and the offending index. As can be seen, ASMA scores correlate with all substance factors and with offending. Of the factor scores, Factor 3 'Socially accepted substances' did not correlate with the other substance factors, but *did* with offending. Factor 1 'Stimulant and Polydrug' correlated positively with offending and negatively with Factor 2 'Addictive type'. The Addictive type factor did *not* correlate significantly with offending.

---

10 Exploratory principal components factor analysis with varimax rotation.

Table 7.1: **Spearman's rank order correlations between measures of substance use and offending**

Measure	ASMA	Factor 1: Stimulant and Polydrug	Factor 2: Addictive type	Factor 3: Socially accepted	Offending score (last 12 months)
ASMA	–	.32	.19	.22	.38
Factor 1: Stimulant and Polydrug		–	-.24	*	.29
Factor 2: Addictive type			–	*	*
Factor 3: Socially accepted				–	.30

Notes: All correlations shown are significant p<0.005
       Non significant correlations are shown as *

Multivariate exploration of the relationship between substance misuse, offending and other risk factors

To explore the relationship between substance misuse and offending further, and the relationship of substance misuse and offending with other risk factors, a series of exploratory linear regression analyses were conducted[11]. As well as the offending index, substance use factors and ASMA score, the regression equations included the following:

- Block 1: Sociodemographics. Age, gender, ethnicity (coded as white or other); whether they had any qualifications or not; school affiliation score[12], and whether the respondent grew up mainly living with both parents, or in some other living arrangement (which most commonly was living with mother only).
- Block 2: Risk and coping. Number of life problems reported as having been experienced ever and life events in the past two years; scores for positive and avoidant coping, and extent hung out with friends near home.

---

11 Stepwise entry design was used, so that only variables that accounted for significant variance were entered.
12 School exclusion was not included as it may be collinear with offending.

- Block 3: Traits and attitudes. Self-esteem score; parental over-protection score; parental care score; parental control score, extent lied to parents; expected earnings aged 25, and extent expected to be in trouble again by age 25.
- Block 4: Substance use (for offending equation). Stimulant and polydrug use, addictive type drug use, socially acceptable drug use, and ASMA score.

In this design of analysis, variables in earlier blocks are assumed to be causally prior to variables in later blocks.

Predictors of offending

Offending in the past 12 months was predicted by a number of risk factors: life events experienced in the past two years (8% of variance), expecting to be in trouble again by 25 (5% of variance) and low positive coping (2% of variance). Offending was also predicted by socially acceptable substance use (9% of variance)[13]. It was surprising that addictive type drugs did not predict offending, so identical analyses were conducted using some common key offences as the dependent variables (again log transformed). Results are shown in Table 7.2. Shoplifting is related to addictive type drug use, whereas stealing from cars and beating people up were related to stimulant and polydrug use. This implies that the classic relationship between heroin or crack use and offending has not disappeared, but that it is swamped in this sample by much more diverse substance use.

---

13 The total adjusted R2 was 0.22.

Table 7.2: *Percentages of offending variance predicted in regression analyses*

Predictor	Frequency in last 12 months			
	Total Offending	Shoplifting	Stealing from cars	Beating up non-family
Age	-	2		-
Gender	-	2	3	-
Low school affiliation score	-	-	5	-
Hangs out near home more	-	-	-	3
More sociable	-	-	-	2
Number of lifetime problems	-	2	-	-
Low positive coping	2	-	-	-
Number of life events in past two years	8	-	8	9
Expects to be in trouble again by age 25	5	6	8	2
Stimulant and Polydrug use	-	-	2	3
Addictive type drug use	-	2	-	-
Socially acceptable drug use	9	-	-	-
TOTAL Adjusted R^2	0.22	0.13	0.26	0.26

Predictors of substance use

Table 7.3 shows predictors of the three substance use factors. As can be seen, stimulant and polydrug use could be only modestly predicted, and socially acceptable substance use could be less well predicted than the other factors. However, all three factors were predicted by similar variables. In the context of normalisation, age only predicted use of addictive type drugs such as heroin and crack.

Table 7.3: *Percentages of substance use variance explained in regression analyses*

Predictor	Factor 1: Stimulant and Polydrug	Factor 2: Addictive type	Factor 3: Socially acceptable
Age	-	3	-
Low school affiliation score	7	4	4
Number of life events in past two years	5	9	3
Expects to be in trouble again by age 25	3	-	-
TOTAL Adjusted R2	0.14	0.15	0.06

Note: All effects shown are significant at p<0.005

Key predictors

Because expecting to be in trouble again and life events appeared to be important predictors of offending and substance use, these variables were explored further.

Expecting to be in trouble again by age 25

Expecting to be in trouble again was correlated with offending, risk factors and some attitude variables. Interestingly, it was unrelated to the number of previous offences. It was related modestly to the number of life events in the past two years (rho=0.20) and lifetime problems (rho=0.23).

Life events

Figure 7.1 shows selected life events experienced in last two years by offending group (as defined in Chapter 6). Only those events that differed significantly across groups are shown. Looking also at the correlations between specific life events and substance use measures, there were many small, significant correlations, but none as large as 0.2. As life event research tends to find, the overall number of events experienced appears to be more important than their exact nature.

Figure 7.1: Life events over the past two years experienced by different offending groups

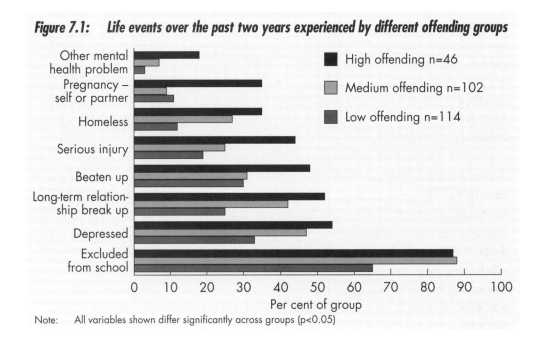

Note: All variables shown differ significantly across groups (p<0.05)

Risk factors associated with those at highest risk of substance misuse problems
Using the ASMA scores, the cohort was divided into those at high risk of a substance misuse problem (15%) and those at medium or low risk. Logistic regression, using the blocks of variables described previously was then used to attempt to predict 'high risk'. This was not successful, only 40 per cent of the high risk group being classified correctly by the analysis. Similar factors to those identified for offending had significant effects: low school affiliation, expecting to be in trouble by age 25, more offending and avoidant style coping.

Substance misuse, offending and use of specialist substance services

Respondents were asked about the extent of their contact with drug or alcohol services in the past two years and the amount of help they had received with drug or alcohol problems in this period (Chapter 5). The latter might not have come from specialist services and may or may not have been needed by the young person. Those who had more than a single contact with a drug or alcohol service tended to use drugs more than those who had no contact or one-off contact, implying that a single contact tended to consist of an assessment leading to no further intervention. Therefore, for comparison purposes, contact was categorised as 'none or a single contact' or 'more than once.' Amount of help was categorised as 'none', 'a little' (very little or a little) and 'some' (some or a lot). Analyses[14] then explored potential relationships between total number of types of offence in 12 months, the three substance use factors and ASMA score (as dependent variables) and contact with drug/alcohol services and amount of help with drug/alcohol use (as independent variables). Only main effects were examined. Contact with services was related only to the Addictive type factor ($F(1,225.2)=9.6$, $p<0.005$), while amount of help was related only to ASMA score ($F(2,201)=6.1$, $p<0.005$).

Thus respondents with more severe substance problems, as defined by ASMA, tended to have received more help, but were likely to have made more than a single contact with a substance service *only* if they were heavier users of heroin, other opiates or crack cocaine. This may be in part because most specialist services are oriented towards users of such drugs. It is also possible that non-specialist staff may be more willing to provide help with substance problems involving what are perceived to be less addictive substances. It is noteworthy, however, that young offenders whose use of alcohol, cannabis and other drugs was extensive, related to offending and to ASMA had not received extended contact with specialist services.

---

14 Multivariate Analyses of Variance

Summary of predicting offending and substance use

- Substance use predicts offending, but socially accepted substances (alcohol, cannabis and tobacco) more so than the use of other drugs, although the latter were less common and hence less able to predict anything.
- Where in the 1980s offenders' drugs of choice often included regular heroin or cocaine, this is no longer so often the case.
- Number of life events in last two years, along with a lack of positive coping mechanisms, predict offending and substance use.
- Low school affiliation predicts offending and substance use.
- Those who currently offended and took substances were more likely to expect to be in trouble again.
- Those with more severe substance problems tended to have received more help, but were likely to have made more than a single contact with a substance service *only* if they were heavier users of addictive type drugs such as heroin, other opiates or crack cocaine.

8   Discussion

Review of main findings

This study has surveyed a cohort of young offenders. It is important to recognise throughout that the cohort cannot be considered to be a representative sample of young offenders, primarily because offenders with less complicated or serious disposals, including most first-time offenders, are under-represented. The practical difficulties of recruiting young people who spent little time engaged with the YOT (and whom all involved were concerned to avoid prematurely stigmatising as 'offenders') suggest that future research should incorporate routes to accessing young offenders other than via YOTs. Although the cohort comprised more serious offenders, in other ways those in it resembled young offenders in general, being predominantly white males aged 15 and 16 (but with some 12 to14 and some 17 or occasionally 18) and having young women represented proportionally. Ethnic minority groups were over-sampled. There were two striking differences between the cohort and young people in general:

- many had been excluded from school, or had dropped out before age 16
- many grew up with their mother only.

Not getting on well at school was directly related to extent of offending and drug use, but growing up with one parent was not.

School exclusion and drop-out is clearly an important contributor to offending and drug use. This study cannot address the form of the relationship and it is worth recognising that it is bound to contain an element of circularity, with drug use and offending likely to lead to exclusion, as well as exclusion providing more opportunities for these behaviours and reducing socially positive alternatives.

Growing up with a single parent did not predict extent of offending or drug use, so why should single parenting predispose to delinquency? This study was not designed to address this question, but it seems likely that having only one parent, while often benign and unremarkable, can sometimes lead to less parental supervision, for there are simply fewer people to provide supervision. Being in a single-parent family is also the consequence of parental separation, which can be more-or-less traumatic for children depending upon the exact circumstances. Such trauma can adversely affect school performance, which in turn may make delinquency more likely. It is also feasible that being from a single-parent family, which is a very visible social feature, results in labelling or stigmatisation, so that young people's behaviour tends to be treated, labelled or sanctioned more negatively by social institutions such as schools and youth justice.

Examining the cohort's personal lives and problems in more detail, a number of important points emerged. First, in addition to high rates of school drop out and exclusion, most of the cohort disliked school and did not get along well there. Second (and this may be related to the first), there were indications of low self-esteem and poor coping skills in the cohort, particularly in not discussing problems with others. School problems and poor coping skills have been often identified as major risk factors for delinquency (e.g. Robins and Rutter, 1990). A third point was that otherwise the cohort perceived their parenting to be normal (with some unease about discussing drugs), had quite normal social lives for their age and slightly lower than normal aspirations for the future. But, fourthly, there were high incidences of potentially traumatic life problems and life events in the cohort, including being a victim of crime as well as a perpetrator. Those who had experienced more life problems and events used substances and offended more.

This profile of difficulties was also reflected in the cohort's service use. For a young cohort, a large proportion had used primary care repeatedly. Accident and emergency department use and social work contacts were also quite prevalent. Repeated service use can indicate psychosocial problems. Looking at use of specialist services, the most common unmet needs were for help with education and getting a job. Apart from the latter, the quality of the help received was generally felt to be low. The emerging pattern, then, is that this cohort of young offenders included many with complex, multiple problems, which could involve extensive service use.

Substance use and offending must be considered against this background. Not surprisingly, given the characteristics documented so far, the cohort was highly delinquent. Most had committed multiple types of offences, repeatedly. For each of the following offences over a fifth of the cohort had committed it more than 20 times: shoplifting, selling stolen goods, taking car without consent, buying drugs, keeping or carrying large quantities of drugs, selling drugs.

Substance use was also very prevalent, with use of every drug being even more prevalent than in the closest comparison group, which was the Youth Lifestyles Survey 'serious' offenders, and much more prevalent than in the British Crime Survey 16 to 30 subsample, despite the younger age of the current cohort. Lifetime prevalence of all drugs was approximately double that of the BCS and the difference was even larger for current (previous year) prevalence, although this may have been partly due to reporting bias. Cannabis, alcohol and tobacco had been used by over 85 per cent of the cohort, 20 to 40 per cent had used amphetamines, ecstasy, cocaine, temazepam, valium, poppers, psilocybin mushrooms and solvents. Less than 20 per cent had used heroin or crack cocaine, but the prevalence of these and other rarer drugs was still above rates in comparable samples. The cohort tended to have tried alcohol, tobacco, cannabis and solvents at similar ages to other samples, generally 11 to 14. The peak age for first trying the remaining drugs (if they had been tried at all) in this cohort was 14, which may be somewhat younger than in previous studies.

Looking also at the frequency of use, tobacco, cannabis and heroin had been used more than 100 days in the preceding 12 months by over 50 per cent of those who had ever used these drugs. This is equivalent to use more than once a week, were use to occur according to a regular pattern. While different social norms are applied to different drugs – 100 days of drinking might be considered moderate, whereas 100 days of heroin might be considered problematic – there is no scientific basis for such distinctions. For most of the other drugs, the majority of users had either not used it during the previous year, or had used less than five days. For alcohol, most had used in the year and use was fairly evenly split across the response categories, with about a quarter using over 100 days in the year. Thus, tobacco and cannabis were both highly prevalent and currently used heavily by many users. Heroin was much less prevalent, but also used heavily by many of its users. Alcohol was prevalent and a large minority was drinking twice a week or more.

When asked to specify a favourite drug, 81 per cent had one, most commonly alcohol or cannabis. The patterns of use of other drugs suggest that they may be of less concern regarding dependence and drug problems for this cohort, although acute problems may still arise. Despite the high prevalence of drug use, few of the cohort reported dependence and this syndrome may not be applicable to this age group. Substance use problems, as assessed by ASMA, appeared to be a more useful way of assessing potential problems and 15 per cent were assessed as at high risk of problems. This is on the one hand quite low, given the high prevalence of drug use in the cohort, but on the other hand is about ten times the proportion assessed at high risk in a school sample (Willner, 2000). Of the cohort, those at high risk were most likely to have been referred or have received other help for a drug problem, but 40 per cent had not received any help. Unfortunately, only a minority of those who received help felt that it had been useful and this applied equally to high, medium and low risk people.

Yet, many people felt that there was some form of relationship between their substance use and their offending. The questions that assessed this were carefully worded to avoid implying that these links were stable or consistent, but many agreed that they had sometimes got into various kinds of trouble while intoxicated and that they had sometimes stolen to get money for alcohol or drugs.

Looking statistically at the relationships between substance use and offending, in this cohort, despite evidence of normalisation, substance use nonetheless predicts offending. However, alcohol, tobacco and cannabis were more related to offending than were other drugs. Where in the 1980s offenders' drugs of choice often included regular heroin or cocaine, this is no longer so often the case. Normalisation may have weakened the specific relationship between opiates and offending. This is not entirely good news, because with a wider range of substances commonly used, there is the potential for a variety of substance use patterns being associated with offending. In the 1980s, for delinquents aged 15 to 17 there may have been a funnelling towards heroin and/or cocaine use and/or drug injection so that by age 17 the most criminal people tended to be drug injectors and/or opiate/cocaine users (Hammersley et al., 1990). In 2001 – 2002 this funnelling had not occurred in this cohort. There are several possible reasons for this.

First, it is possible that the cohort is too young for this funnelling to have yet occurred, although they are no younger than the purposive community sample recruited by Hammersley et al. (1990). If funnelling is yet to occur, then this should be detected in the second wave of the study.

Second, as the present cohort was obtained from a wide variety of areas around the country, it is possible that widespread heroin and cocaine use remain restricted to specific places, while drug use in general has spread and normalised everywhere. Funnelling can only occur where heroin, cocaine and injecting are widespread. Elsewhere delinquents primarily use other drugs, notably alcohol and cannabis. Arrestee data from New ADAM (Patton, 2002) indicate that there are substantial local variations in drug prevalence. Unfortunately, the present cohort did not contain enough heroin users, cocaine users or injectors to be able to examine local variations. In the 1980s, most research attention was upon heroin and cocaine users/injectors, hence undertaken in areas of high prevalence. The findings from those areas may not generalise to areas where these drug practices are rarer.

Third, being arrested, hence becoming an 'official' young offender, and extensive drug use may both be signs of a period of intense misbehaviour which may or may not be permanent, but does not necessarily involve heroin or cocaine use, or injecting. This will be discussed further below.

Fourth, the cohort is of young offenders who have been detected. Studies of offending by drug users tend to include large numbers of undetected offenders. It is possible that young heroin/cocaine users or injectors are relatively unlikely to be arrested. This may be ruled out as being both ad hoc and contradicting evidence that such drug users can be persistent, high frequency criminals who therefore acquire an arrest history.

Fifth, people may be more likely to under-report heroin use, cocaine use and drug injecting than to under-report other drug practices (Patton, 2002). It could be that substantial numbers of this cohort have admitted drug and alcohol use but have minimised or denied heroin or cocaine use, or injecting. Biological testing was not feasible in this study as it was thought likely to jeopardise consent. Data from the second wave may illuminate the problem, as if the cohort contains covert heroin or cocaine users then these may become overt if they develop more problems over time.

Whichever of these explanations are correct, it is an important fact that drug use by young offenders involves cannabis and alcohol use, so interventions need to address these substances as well as others. Currently, engagement with drug services beyond a single contact – i.e. assessment – tends to occur only for users of heroin, other opiates or crack cocaine. The reasons for this are not clear, but imply that in some sense services are inappropriate for other types of drug user, which will be discussed further below. If a message is commonly being conveyed that intense cannabis and alcohol use require no more than single session intervention, then this needs to be redressed.

Even in this selected cohort, that was highly criminal and included extensive users of drugs, two types of risk factor predicted the extent of both substance use and offending. First, low affiliation with school and, second, having had more traumatic life events in the last two years along with a lack of positive coping mechanisms. In other words young people who are not flourishing at school and who have had stressful things happen to them offend and take drugs more. This implies a need to teach young offenders – as well as other young people – positive coping mechanisms, including mechanisms for dealing with past events and overcoming trauma.

A key question, to be addressed in the second wave of this work, is to identify when this pattern of intense and dysfunctional behaviour is a temporary lapse and when and why it goes on to become a career of drug problems and crime.

Implications

Patterns of behaviour

This report has found evidence of extensive substance use by young offenders, across the whole range of drugs and other substances that are commonly misused. While there appear to be links between substance use and offending, these are complex and mediated by adverse life events, risk factors and coping. High levels of substance use amongst young offenders do not indicate that many of them are dependent upon heroin, cocaine (or anything else) at this point. The normalisation of drug use may have diversified the possible pathways through drug use, so that becoming a criminal heroin or cocaine 'addict' is no longer a typical route, even if it still occurs for some.

Three forms of drug use found here merit particular concern. First, the very high prevalence of smoking of both cannabis and tobacco is worrying, particularly in combination with alcohol. Many respondents felt that intoxication had led to acute problems related to offending. Second, the prevalence of temazepam and diazepam (valium) is worrying as they may form a bridge between the so-called 'recreational' drugs and injectables. Third, cocaine is much more widely used than heroin. A caution here is that people may under-report cocaine (particularly crack) and heroin in a criminal justice context.

Some key factors were related to both substance use and offending: life difficulties and events, disliking and being excluded from school, lack of positive coping mechanisms and expecting to get into trouble again. These factors suggest that there can be a risk of a vicious circle developing where drugs and perhaps offending are used to cope with life's difficulties, which can make those difficulties worse, which can confirm young people's expectations of getting into trouble again. This is liable to progressively detach them from conventional social values. Education has a key role here. Generally, the cohort wanted to acquire qualifications, despite having had difficulties with school and many having been excluded or having dropped out.

Service use and service needs

The cohort felt that they had received quite a lot of help, but the quality was generally perceived to be low. Because of the diversity of substance use in this cohort, it is as well to be wary of generic programmes tackling such problems. Individual or small-scale interventions may be more appropriate. However, research of this kind can only make generic suggestions for intervention. First, as well as addressing offending and substance using behaviour, there is a need to address coping with life difficulties. When confronted with life difficulties, then those with poorer coping skills may adopt an escape based on immediate excitement and hedonism involving drugs and offending. To quote an ex-heroin user from another study:

'It's like replacing all the other problems with one great big problem.' (Mullen *et al.*, in press)

Addressing the smaller problems and teaching coping is not easy with people adopting this tactic. Furthermore, in this cohort the 'smaller' problems could include those with far-reaching effects, such as school exclusion, and traumatic events such as bereavement. In this context, trying to define drug use as 'the problem' may be unproductive, because clients may consider it to be the solution to other problems.

There is also a need for more services that deal effectively with mid-range substance use problems (Tier 2) in this age group. There have been recent attempts to develop substance services for young offenders (Hammersley *et al.*, in press), which encountered a number of problems.

Assessment

Assessment of substance use in young offenders is problematic, because they are ambivalent about their drug use and concerned that adults, particularly their parents, may over-react. In addition, not all non-specialist staff are sophisticated about drugs and so may fail to probe sufficiently to differentiate any use of illegal drugs at all from problem drug use. Another concern is that assessment can be superficial sometimes to avoid making work, delays and difficulties for everyone. ASMA would be extremely helpful here, but training would be required to score and use it appropriately. A more fundamental problem is that judgements about the severity of a substance use problem cannot be made independently of the young person's offending history. It is important to avoid confusing periods of intense behaviour, where drugs do not cause offending in any straightforward way, with drug dependence where they can.

Engagement

Most drug services are sophisticated about drug use amongst young people and wary of simplistic labels and formulaic interventions. They may routinely work with the young client on a range of issues and may prioritise concerns other than drugs, such as employment, education and family issues. Nonetheless, even with best practice, it can be difficult to engage young people with services, because they are ambivalent about their problems and understandably wary of being labelled as having a drugs problem. Even amongst those assessed at high risk for drug problems, two-thirds of those who had not received help with their substance use felt that they did not need any. Systemic approaches involving the family can be helpful here (Liddle and Dakhoff, 1995) and may also ease concerns about parents over-reacting, and young people under-reacting, to drug problems. Family and systemic approaches are not yet widely used in the UK for drug problems and the costs may be a barrier to widespread use.

Content of interventions
Despite the sophistication of drug services, many are less experienced with younger clients and available packaged interventions may not match contemporary needs. There are educational interventions intended for non-users and drug experimenters, with a view to warning about, delaying and reducing substance use. These are irrelevant for young offenders as represented by this cohort. There are also harm reduction interventions intended for active, recreational users. Unfortunately, while some of this cohort may be recreational users, others have moved beyond this to problematic use. Even if this is due to an intense period of life, rather than nascent dependence, advice about safe practices, moderation and so on may not be well-received. Finally, there are interventions for abuse and dependence, but these can be of limited relevance to young people who have yet to experience the full consequences of dependence, if they ever will. Interventions with young offenders need to address current motives for and use habits, rather than focussing on specific substances, or on harm reduction and prevention.

There is also a need for interventions designed to address substance use, offending, school problems, life traumas and coping skills in an integrated way without necessarily considering the drug problem to be primary. It may be a moot point as to whether such integrated interventions are best provided by a 'drugs service'.

General service issues
There is a need to consider the complexities surrounding the relationship between substance use and other problems in young offenders. It is tempting to fall into such thinking, because it is one way of prioritising services, but for most young offenders at least substance abuse is neither the main cause of their other problems, nor a subsidiary symptom that will naturally vanish when the other problems are treated. This cohort could not be neatly divided into normal substance users without problems and 'addicts' with problems.

It is rather beyond the remit of this research, but for young patients, GP health behaviour screenings need nowadays to consider drugs as well as drinking and smoking. Stigma and anxiety on both sides make this difficult. Other generalists, such as social workers, also need to enquire routinely about substance use when other problems are evident.

Parents need to be engaged concerning their children's substance use. It may be easier to do this when that use is predominantly alcohol, cannabis and tobacco, rather than focussing too much on the drugs perceived to be more serious. Such a focus can lead to complacency amongst parents whose children avoid the stigmatised drugs and panic amongst those whose children are known to use them. Neither response is appropriate. Data from this cohort (who are relatively serious drug users) suggest that ages 11 to 14 are important for drug experimentation. Part of engaging parents will be teaching them a sad realism about the contemporary prevalence of drug use in this age group. This includes recognition that broad experimentation is a common part of adolescent drug use and appreciation that immoderate use of any substance should be of concern. One suspects that parents generally hope for too long that it is other people's children of this age who are using drugs.

Many schools adopt a low- or zero-tolerance to drug use. This may not be helpful as it encourages children to conceal, rather than deal with, their drug use and can lead to the exclusion of those caught, who are not necessarily those who use drugs most, never mind the only users in school.

To conclude on a more theoretical note, this study has broadly confirmed that drug use has become normalised amongst young offenders, but with the strong caveat that 'normalisation' does not indicate some problem-free activity that society is merely prejudiced about. As evidenced by this survey, young offenders drink and take drugs not only more than their peers, but far more than society should approve of, or they should want to. The long-term impact of this remains to be ascertained.

Appendix A   Pilot work

Pilot work was undertaken to inform procedures for accessing and recruiting participants, ethical considerations, and development of the questionnaire.

Informing procedures for accessing and recruiting participants

Pilot work was undertaken with one YOT in Essex, and began to highlight some of the challenges that would be later encountered in the main study. Most noticeable was the length of time required to obtain initial agreement for the research to take place.

Participation in the research was entirely voluntary and a £15 CD voucher was offered as an incentive. Recruitment of participants was undertaken by YOT workers using an eye-catching leaflet outlining the project and what would be involved, and asking the young person to provide contact details if s/he was willing to take part. The young person was then telephoned by a researcher and a meeting arranged, usually to take place at the YOT premises. Key learning from this pilot work included:

- Recruitment into the study was much slower than anticipated and respondents not attending appointments was a major problem.
- YOT staff needed to be fully briefed about the research and be 'on-side'.
- YOT staff needed to understand that all young offenders could take part (piloting revealed a tendency for YOT staff to screen youngsters for 'suitability').
- Publicity needed to be as wide as possible through the use of posters etc.
- Value existed of basing a researcher 'full-time' at the YOT (at least at those YOTs where work with youngsters is undertaken onsite).
- There was a need to identify alternative organisations through which young offenders can be accessed.
- Value emerged of creating opportunities for young people to complete the questionnaire at the time they agree to take part, rather than having to return for a specific meeting (although issues of parental consent must be considered).

Informing ethical considerations

The project was granted ethical approval by the University of Essex. Pilot work informed the protocol for ensuring that informed consent was properly obtained, and the development of procedures for obtaining parent/carer consent for those under the age of 16.

Informed consent

An information sheet was prepared detailing the purpose of the research, what would be entailed, and the rights of participants. Pilot work revealed that the most effective way of ensuring participants understood the information was for the researcher to 'talk through' each of the points, and then by giving the participant time to read the information before being asked to sign to confirm consent.

Parent/carer consent

Parent/carer consent was initially sought for all participants under the age of 16. Pilot work revealed this approach to be unworkable, however. The chaotic lifestyles of many young people who offend, and their families, meant that often the necessary paperwork went astray, and frequently potential participants would be lost due to time delays. As YOT staff commonly act as 'appropriate adults' for the young people it seemed reasonable that they could provide consent instead, and this was agreed by the University of Essex. In the main study, staff of the various YOTs and researcher teams had differing views about the acceptability of this approach, but ultimately, consent for all participants aged under 16 was provided by either a parent/carer or a YOT worker responsible for the young person's care.

Informing questionnaire development

The eight young people who completed the questionnaire during the pilot phase were asked to discuss their thoughts while completing the questions. In this way, young people's comprehension of the questions could be assessed, and problematic questions identified. As a result, minor changes in wording were made, additional questions were included to allow people who had recently given up drugs to report their behaviour prior to giving up and a number of questions were removed to keep the interview about an hour long.

Appendix B   Challenges of accessing young offenders

The challenges faced in recruiting a sufficiently large sample for this study to be viable were considerable and related to three areas.

The YOTs

- Some YOTs felt 'over-researched' and access was refused by some YOTs identified for the original sample. In other cases it was necessary to access the young people via linked organisations.
- Staff were not always able to devote the energy required to encouraging youngsters to take part.
- It was easier to access young people in YOTs where many activities were based at YOT premises, than at those YOTs where much work was undertaken on an outreach basis.

The young people

- Many young people referred to YOTs live chaotic lives and often missed appointments.
- For some, the incentive of a £15 CD voucher was insufficient.
- The fact that the target group was 'young people referred to Youth Offending Teams' served as a disincentive for some, who wanted as little association with the YOT as possible. This may have led to the eventual sample under-representing those with less YOT involvement, such as those on Final Warnings without additional requirements attached to the order.
- Peer pressure could work in favour of or against participation. If peer group leaders were recruited and developed a positive attitude to the research, this improved recruitment. In contrast, if leaders found completing the questionnaire a negative experience, recruitment plummeted.

The fieldwork teams

Various models of team working evolved, with data collection:

- managed and undertaken by one local researcher
- managed locally by academics supervising other researchers
- managed locally by DAAT Project Officers supervising drug agency staff supervising volunteer data collectors (this was necessary where YOTs insisted that data collectors were police checked)
- by researchers supervised directly by the Essex team.

These different models, combined with the varying amounts of time data collectors were able to devote to the fieldwork, varying levels of commitment from different YOTs, and the variety of working practices within the YOTs, meant that strategies to maximise success were developed according to the combination of circumstances in each geographical area. Most successful was a model whereby:

- recruitment began immediately access was agreed (perhaps most importantly)
- negotiations with YOT staff and recruitment were undertaken by the same person
- most offenders visited the YOT premises regularly
- the researcher was able to locate his/herself at the YOT full-time for the data collection period.

Appendix C   Education/employment status

Age left school and employment status	No.		%	
At school – no job (or no information about job)	86		29	
At school & part-time job	14	} 112	5	} 38
Left school 16+ & at college & part-time job	2		1	
Left school 16+ & at college (no job)	10		3	
Left school before 16 & on training scheme & full-time job	2		1	
Left school before 16 & on training scheme & part-time job	5		2	
Left school before 16 & on training scheme (no job)	24	} 42	8	} 14
Left school 16+ & on training scheme & part-time job	1		*	
Left school 16+ & on training scheme & full-time job	4		1	
Left school 16+ & on training scheme (no job)	6		2	
Left school before 16 & full-time job	4		1	
Left school before 16 & part-time job	5		2	
Left school 16+ & full-time job	6	} 17	2	} 6
Left school 16+ & part-time job	1		*	
Left school 16+ & job (unspecified full or part-time)	1		*	
Left school before 16 – no education or employment	83	} 105	28	} 36
Left school 16+ - no education or employment	22		8	
Unclassifiable	10		3	
No answer	7		2	
Total	293		100	

Appendix D   Offences ever committed

Offence	Men (n=237)		Women (n=56)		All (n=293)	
	No	%	No	%	No	%
Damaged or destroyed, purposely or recklessly, something belonging to someone else	196	83	44	79	240	82
Stolen anything from a shop, supermarket or department store	187	79	48	86	235	80
Taken part in fighting or disorder in a group in a public place	170	72	38	68	208	71
Bought something that you knew, or believed at the time, was stolen	170	72	35	63	205	70
Sold something that you knew, or believed at the time, was stolen*	172	73	32	57	204	70
Stolen anything out of or from a car**	156	66	23	41	179	61
Bought drugs for other people	145	61	33	59	178	61
Set fire, purposely or recklessly, to something not belonging to you	135	57	28	50	163	56
Hurt someone with a knife, stick or other weapon*	138	58	23	41	161	55
Taken away a bicycle without the owner's permission, not intending to give it back**	137	58	14	25	151	52
Sneaked into someone's garden or house or a building intending to steal something	124	52	23	41	147	50
Taken away a car without the owner's permission, not intending to give it back*	123	52	20	36	143	49
Taken away a motorbike or moped without the owner's permission, not intending to give it back**	121	51	10	18	131	45
Stolen anything in school worth more than £5*	105	44	14	25	119	41
Stolen anything worth more than £5, not mentioned already*	103	44	15	27	118	40
Stolen money from a gas or electricity meter, public telephone, vending machine, video game or fruit machine	98	41	17	30	115	39
Threatened someone with a weapon or with beating them up to get money or other valuables from them	88	37	18	32	106	36
Used a chequebook, credit card, cash-point card (ATM card) that you knew or believed at the time to be stolen to get money out of a bank account	50	21	19	34	69	24

Offence	Men (n=237)		Women (n=56)		All (n=293)	
	No	%	No	%	No	%
Stolen anything from a place that you worked worth more than £5	57	24	10	18	67	23
Pick-pocketed anything from anybody	35	15	11	20	46	16
Sold a chequebook, credit card, cash-point card (ATM card) belonging to you or someone else so that they could steal money from a bank account	35	15	10	18	45	15
Claimed more than £5 in expenses that you knew that you were not entitled to	27	11	1	2	28	10
Snatched from someone a purse, bag or something else	36	15	18	32	54	18
Claimed social security benefits to which you knew that you were not entitled	14	6	2	4	16	6
Made false claim on an insurance poiicy	11	5	1	2	12	4
Made an incorrect tax return	4	2	1	2	5	2
Beaten up someone not belonging to your immediate family to such an extent that you think or know that medical help or a doctor was needed	117	49	22	39	139	47
Beaten up someone in your immediate family to such an extent that you think or know that medical help or a doctor was needed	33	14	12	21	45	15
Sold drugs to other people for money	112	47	24	43	136	46
Kept or carried large quantities of drugs	107	45	25	45	132	45
Solicited, that is, offered or invited sex in exchange for money	6	3	3	5	9	3

Notes: Between 0 and three respondents did not provide an answer for each item.
Sex difference * p<0.05; ** p<0.005.

Appendix E   Questions used in the Assessment of Substance Misuse in Adolescents (ASMA) (Willner 2000)

Respondents answer yes, no or 'I do not use drugs' to the following:

If you use drugs, do you have a favourite drug you use?

If you use drugs, do you ever do so alone?

Do you use drugs because you're bored, lonely or anxious?

If you use drugs, do you think a lot about drugs and drug use?

Do you plan your day to make sure you can use drugs?

Do you need to use more and more drugs to get high?

Do you feel irritable or anxious if you don't use drugs?

Do you miss your favourite drug if you don't use it for a while?

An instruction was included to make it explicit that the term 'drugs' included alcohol.

Appendix F

Results of a factor analysis of frequency of substance use in past 12 months

Substance	Factor 1: Stimulant and Polydrug 36% variance	Factor 2: Addictive type 14% variance	Factor 3: Socially accepted 9% variance
Alcohol	.37	-.56	.37
Amphetamines	.78		
Cannabis	.42	-.38	.52
Cocaine	.71		
Crack cocaine	.63	.31	
Ecstasy	.75		
Heroin	.32	.76	
LSD	.77		
Methadone	.31	.77	
Poppers	.56		-.33
Mushrooms	.79		
Solvents	.67		
Temazepam	.70		
Tobacco			.70
Valium	.60	.31	

Notes: Figures shown are individual substances' loadings on the factors identified in the factor analysis. Loadings < 0.3 have been deleted from the table for clarity.

References

Aldridge, J., Parker, H. and Measham, F. (1999) *Drug trying and drug use across adolescence. A longitudinal study of young people's drug taking in two regions of northern England.* London, Home Office, Drug Prevention and Advisory Service, Paper 1.

American Psychiatric Association (1994) *Diagnostic and Statistical Manual of Mental Disorders – 4th Edition* (DSM-IV). Washington, APA.

CACI (2002) Wealth of the Nation, Summary. http://www.caci.co.uk/pdfs/Wealth%20of%20the%20Nation%202002%20-%20Summary%20Copy.pdf (accessed 29.10.02)

Carver, C.S., Scheier, M.F. and Weintraub, J.K. (1989) *Assessing coping strategies: a theoretically-based approach.* Journal of Personality and Social Psychology, 56, 267-283.

Davies, J.B. (1997) *The Myth of Addiction*, 2nd edition. London, Psychology Press.

Elliott, D.S., Huizinga, D. and Ageton, S.S. (1985) *Explaining delinquency and drug use.* London, Sage.

Farrington, D. (1996) *Understanding Juvenile Delinquency*, York, Joseph Rowntree Foundation.

Fergusson, D.M. and Horwood, L.J. (2000) Does cannabis use encourage other forms of illicit drug use? *Addiction*, 95, 505-520.

Flood-Page, C., Campbell, S., Harrington, V. and Miller, J. (2000) Youth Crime: *Findings from the 1998/99 Youth Lifestyles Survey.* London, Home Office, Home Office Research Study 209.

Gossop, M., Griffiths, P., Powis, B. and Strang, J. (1992) Severity of dependence and route of administration of heroin, cocaine and amphetamines. *British Journal of Addiction*, 87, 1527-1536.

Goulden, C. and Sondhi, A. (2001) *At the margins: Drug use by vulnerable young people in the 1998/1989 Youth Lifestyles Survey.* London, CRU, Home Office.

Graham, J. and Bowling, B. (1996) *Young people and crime.* Research Study 145. London, Home Office Research and Statistics Directorate.

Hammersley, R. (1994) A digest of memory phenomena for addiction research. *Addiction,* 89, 283-293.

Hammersley, R., Forsyth, A.J.M, Morrison, V.L. and Davies, J.B. (1989) The relationship between crime and opioid use. *British Journal of Addiction,* 84, 1029-1043.

Hammersley, R., Forsyth, A.J.M and Lavelle, T.L. (1990) The criminality of new drug users in Glasgow. *British Journal of Addiction,* 85, 1583-1594.

Hammersley, R., Minkes, J., Reid, M., Oliver, A., Genova, A. and Raynor, P. (in press) *Drug and alcohol projects for young offenders: the evaluation of development fund projects funded by the Youth Justice Board.* London, Youth Justice Board.

Holdaway, S., Davidson, N., Dignan, J., Hammersley, R., Hine, J. and Marsh, P. (2001) *New strategies to address youth offending: The national evaluation of the pilot youth offending teams.* Research Development Statistics Occasional Paper no. 69. London: Home Office. http://www.homeoffice.gov.uk/rds/pdfs/occ69-newstrat.pdf

Liddle, H.A. and Dakoff, G.A. (1995) Family-based treatment for adolescent drug use: state of the science. In *Adolescent Drug Abuse: Clinical Assessment and Therapeutic Interventions.* Rahdert, E. and Czechowicz, D. (eds) NIDA Research Monograph 156, Rockville MD, National Institute on Drug Abuse. 218-254.

Mullen, K., Hammersley, R. and Marriott, C. (in press) "After you've ran with the rats the mice are a bore." Cessation of heroin use amongst men entering mid-life. In Palacious, W. and Cromwell, P. (2003) *Cocktails and Dreams: An interpretative perspective on drug use.* New Jersey, Prentice-Hall.

Parker, G., Tupling, H. and Brown, L.B. (1979) A parental bonding instrument. *British Journal of Medical Psychology,* 52, 1-10.

Parker, H., Aldridge, J. and Measham, F. (1998) *Illegal Lesiure. The normalization of adolescent recreational drug use.* London, Routledge.

Patton, D.J. (2002) *You want the truth? You can't handle the truth. An exploration of the reporting practices of drug use among arrestees in the context of normalization.* Unpublished PhD thesis, School of Law, University of Sheffield.

Ramsay, M., Baker, P., Goulden, C., Sharp, C. and Sondhi, A. (2001) *Drug misuse declared in 2000: results from the British Crime Survey.* London, Home Office.

Robins, L. and Rutter, M. (1990) *Straight and devious pathways from childhood to adulthood.* Cambridge, Cambridge University Press.

Rosenberg, M. (1965) *Society and the Adolescent Self-Image.* Princeton, New Jersey, Princeton University Press.

Williams, A. (1998) *Alcohol use and abuse: the role of escape drinking.* Unpublished PhD thesis, Department of Psychology, University of Wales, Swansea.

Willner, P. (2000) Further validation and development of a screening instrument for the assessment of substance misuse in adolescents. *Addiction*, 95, 1691-1698.

RDS Publications

Requests for Publications

Copies of our publications and a list of those currently available may be obtained from:

> Home Office
> Research, Development and Statistics Directorate
> Communication Development Unit
> Room 275, Home Office
> 50 Queen Anne's Gate
> London SW1H 9AT
> Telephone: 020 7273 2084 (answerphone outside of office hours)
> Facsimile: 020 7222 0211
> E-mail: publications.rds@homeoffice.gsi.gov.uk

alternatively

why not visit the RDS web-site at
> Internet: http://www.homeoffice.gov.uk/rds/index.htm

where many of our publications are available to be read on screen or downloaded for printing.